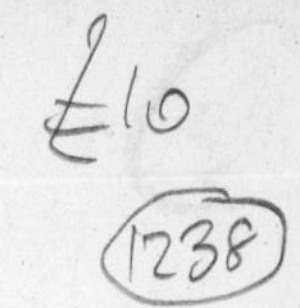

PROPHECY OF FAMINE

PROPHECY OF FAMINE

A Warning and the Remedy

H. J. MASSINGHAM AND
EDWARD HYAMS

THAMES AND HUDSON
London

FIRST PUBLISHED 1953

PRINTED IN GREAT BRITAIN BY
THE CAMELOT PRESS LTD LONDON AND SOUTHAMPTON

Contents

Preface

BY MRS. H. J. MASSINGHAM

IN justice to my husband I feel I ought to stress the point that Mr. Hyams makes in his Foreword: that he never saw the last two and mainly political chapters in which Mr. Hyams—for whom he had a great admiration—recommends the nationalization of the land. I am certain from my knowledge of my husband's views up to the last hour of his life that he would never have lent his support to such a proposal, for it was contrary to everything in which he believed. His love for the land made him hate much that Mr. Hyams hates—the exploiter, the unconscionable middleman and the commercial violator of the soil—but it did not make him a Socialist or a believer in Socialism. He was essentially non-political. To him the land was a matter of such vital importance—to quote his own words—"as to be above and below politics". Of the responsible landowner, as of all other responsible individuals, he was an unfailing champion, and a lifelong critic of all large-scale bureaucratic organization. But he greatly respected Mr. Hyams's views, and I know Mr. Hyams respects his. The latter has, therefore, asked me to add this preface on behalf of one who can no longer speak for himself.

PENELOPE MASSINGHAM

Foreword

BY EDWARD HYAMS

In the early summer of 1952 I suggested to H. J. Massingham that he should write this book, which badly needed writing; and to Thames and Hudson that they should publish it. Both agreed, but Massingham made one condition: that of the eight chapters we sketched together, I must write four. I was moved by being invited to collaborate with a man whose writing I admired, whose integrity I respected and many of whose opinions I shared.

This Foreword is made necessary by the most unhappy fact of Massingham's death, which occurred at a time when world events had begun to vindicate the ideas and opinions he had been developing during twenty years and more. Had he lived it would probably not have been necessary for me to make the following explanations.

Massingham was generally supposed to be a reactionary. In so far as my name is known at all, which is not widely, it is as that of a socialist. How came we to collaborate so readily and with so much pleasure and mutual advantage? In the first place, any socialist who has read history is a reactionary: he looks back to a time when, for example, all land was held in common by the community and when duty towards the State in the person of the monarch as the servant of the people, was universally accepted. It is open to him, unless he be a strict and doctrinaire Marxist, to regard the rise of capitalism as a kind of crime against humanity by men who threw off the sense of responsibility towards the community, to serve their own ends; or as an aberration which interrupted the progress of man towards a wider community.

H. J. Massingham was certainly a reactionary in the sense that he thought Britain's social and cultural past nobler and more properly human than her present. But because the very word *reaction* is associated, rightly or wrongly, with political "conservatism", Massingham was also supposed to be a Conservative. Nothing could be farther from the truth, which was that he fully realized that the Conservative Party was as hostile to the values he respected, as any Socialist Party could be. Not only was there very little in modern, upper-class Britain that he could respect, he expressed in the strongest language, in conversation as in print, his loathing and detestation of capitalist-industrialism, the arch-enemy of what he believed to be the good kind of life. And if he also loathed socialism it was because he supposed it must simply exaggerate and emphasize the economic trends he thought pernicious, and not at all for its social content. As to that, as an admirer and historian of the Manorial system, he was so far from being committed to a system of "free" economy, that he believed in duty, service, responsibility as the motives which should keep society working, not in profit.

It was over an article of mine in the *New Statesman and Nation*, "Soil and Socialism", that we met. He was enthusiastic about it. The idea that socialism might be based upon farming, upon land, instead of upon the factory, and that such a socialism must necessarily restore some of the fine values he lived and wrote for, was new to him and delighted him. He agreed to write this book not only because he felt that yet another warning of possible, and indeed probable famine should be published; but also because he saw the possibility that in turning back to her land, Britain might be saved in more senses than one. What he felt about that is to be found in the *Envoi* to this book.

We collaborated, then, because we agreed about so much that our disagreements were insignificant. In the course of writing the book our meetings were few, our letters many. What each of us wrote or was to write was thoroughly discussed between us. It would be impossible to imagine a more sympathetic, warm-hearted, generous and patient collaborator than Massingham. No one could have listened more courteously, and argued more thoughtfully, when we disagreed; no one could have accepted victory more reluctantly when it was I who yielded; or yielded more eagerly and gracefully when I maintained my point.

Before he died, Massingham had finished his four chapters which, as most readers will discover for themselves, are Nos. III, V, VI, and VIII. I have done no more than tidy them, but I know that their author would have wished me to thank Mr. Jorian Jenks for the care with which he read the typescript and suggested amendments, though Massingham in his then state of health was unable to revise his work with his usual thoroughness. Massingham had also read and approved two of my chapters, approved the sketches of two more. And not many days before he died we sat together on his terrace, under his vine, looking out over the beautiful garden which he and his wife had made, and, despite the fact that he was very ill, we discussed, at his instance, Chapter IX.

I do not wish to imply that he approved of all my ideas. He was so warm-hearted that it was painful for him to argue against any man he liked, but nevertheless he was deeply distrustful of the intellectual leaders of socialism and he resented the fact that they had never attempted to understand his own ideas. Yet he saw and admitted that to save herself from famine Britain must use science and industry in the service of agriculture, that there was no going back. He insisted only that these servants should remain servants, not become masters, and that science should be used, not abused. He saw, too, that if the values he believed in were to be restored, it must be in modern terms. He had long realized that the political Right Wing represented an industry, a commerce and a finance he abhorred and blamed. And he allowed me, with a tolerant but slightly sceptical smile, to convince him that the, to him, equally graceless and blind opponents of the evil trinity, the men of the political Left, might not be quite so hopelessly committed to the past, so incapable of seeing the future in any but super-nineteenth-century terms.

Let me make it very clear, however, that Massingham never read Chapters VII and IX. Perhaps had he done so he might have persuaded me to make changes, but I have tried very hard to put into them nothing which, however it might have offended him in some ways, he would not have wished me to publish as my belief. I do not wish to misrepresent the ideas and feelings of a man who is, most unhappily, no longer here to explain them; nor to publish my own under our joint names and give the impression that he shared all of them.

EDWARD HYAMS

CHAPTER I

When shall We Starve?

WHEN SHALL we starve, we in Britain? Quite soon. The answer cannot be put more exactly than that because we cannot estimate the ingenuity of politicians in finding expedients and evasions which enable them to put off the day of famine, to scrape up a bit of meat here and a handful of corn there, and so to keep going for another few weeks or months. But the fact itself is clear and the object of this book is to make it equally so to the men and women who live in cities and are forced to put their trust for their daily bread and meat in the abilities and foresight of men who have little of either. You, the readers of this book, have been consistently misled by politicians and experts of all parties who are either ignorant of the facts themselves, or too harassed by immediate and terrifying responsibilities beyond the power of their weary minds to face.

It is vital that you, to whom this book is addressed, should understand clearly the situation in which we, in Britain, are placed. This is not another pronouncement about the dollar gap, the permanent state of war, the rising cost of living—and dying. It is about food. There is not enough of it left in the world. If people told you this, you could do something about it. But you are not told; you are being left until, one day, you will suddenly be informed by your newspaper that there is a far worse crisis than any yet experienced; that there is to be bread rationing on a stringent scale; that the meat ration is to be cut by half or more. From that moment it may no longer be a question of shortages, but perhaps of famine. We may even live in a world in which the majority of children have the aged, haggard faces of the old, and the swollen bellies of starvation; a time of declining health, of people engaged in little, harassing black market deals for a quarter of a pound of butter or half a dozen eggs; of doctors, themselves underfed, shrugging tired shoulders helplessly over the immense queue of patients all suffering from the same disease—starvation.

Such may well be the prospect before us.

*

But this book is neither a jeremiad nor a proclamation of woe. There would certainly be no point whatsoever in telling you that you, and your children, certainly your children and grandchildren, are going to rot of starvation, if we, the authors, did not think that there was a way of avoiding this. Our aims are: to persuade you that we are talking sense; to point out how to avoid famine; and to get you to insist on action. You. Not your leaders. You will have to pull yourselves together and do your own leading for a change. We believe that in the process of avoiding famine in these islands, we can also found a new society so firmly and soundly based that nothing but an H-bomb can shake it again; that it will be, by its very nature, secure against the economic storms which come from east and west. There is no *need* for Britain to starve; there is no *need* for us to go running humbly to the Argentine for beef, only to be humiliated; or to subsist on a dole paid with weary contempt by Americans who, in their heart of hearts, are sure we are finished, and wish to goodness we would get on with dying, like the troublesome poor relation we have become.

*

First of all, for the benefit of those readers who are saying to themselves, *What on earth is all this?* and who are already regarding us, the authors, as a couple of crazy cranks proclaiming famine in a world crammed with food: what is this mess of food-bankruptcy into which Britain has floundered? To answer that we shall take the risk of being accused of oversimplification. We know here and now, what will be said to you about our arguments, unless they are simply ignored. The real experts—you know the men, with their quiet and confident manner, their rather neat suits, their gently sardonic smile, their polite refusal to argue, their little shrug of deprecation—will say, *Oh well, you know, Hyams and Massingham . . . muck and mysticism . . . of course, there's something in what they say, but, like all amateurs, they've only got hold of a bit of the story. Of course, we could go into it for you if you like . . . but it's all rather complicated, and hardly worth your while. Just get on with filling up your football pool coupon and leave all that to us.* Yes, we are ready for that. And here, to begin with, is what we believe all but a few exceptional men among these experts are like: they are neither ignorant nor malicious nor even actually irresponsible. They are, simply, like most people. They argue, to themselves, in the small hours, when they lie awake and feel small and frightened by the facts they know . . . they say to themselves: *On the face of it, there will be famine in Britain within, say, fifteen years—but no, it won't happen, because I cannot conceive of it happening. Something will turn up. The scientists will . . .*

And there it is . . . the pipe dream of us all. Is there threat of atomic bombs? Never mind, the scientists will invent an umbrella to keep them off. Is there a drought? Science will make it rain. Is there a flood? Science will dry it up. Science . . . it has become the witch doctor we all believe in and are afraid of. And its results are about as reliable. We ought to depict science as a terrifying figure attired in a nylon imitation leopard skin dancing before our frightened and hypnotized eyes with a skull in one hand—of someone who has died of atom-bomb radiation, or DDT poisoning—and a wand in the other made of synthetic bread.

But such are the scientists *we* have made. The real ones can be useful enough . . . provided we don't allow them to put on a bishop's cope and mitre and pretend to be high priests. Real science can save the world from starvation . . . in about a hundred years of hard work and with about as much money as we now squander on armaments. But that is not our problem. Our problem is to feed Britain now.

What follows is a rough and short summary in simple terms of how Britain has got into such a mess. It is simplified, not because we wish to insult the reader's intelligence, but because if he or she is not at all acquainted with economic and farming history, then, in such matters, he or she will be as much of a child as we should be if it was a question of making a pair of shoes, or auditing accounts.

*

For many centuries up to and, in most places, including the early 19th century, the normal organization of Western communities was roughly as follows: The soil of each country was cultivated by small farmers who either owned it, or were tenants of some great landlord, or were members of communities which owned the land in common, the nominal owner being the Crown. The objects of these farmers were two:

(1) To grow food and raw materials to feed, clothe and house their families.

(2) To grow a surplus of food and raw materials over and above the things needed in their own parish, which they could sell to townsmen, and with the money thus earned buy such goods as were made in towns, and such services as the towns rendered, and so enjoy a higher standard of living.

The system was very local and parochial. There was little exchange, little trade. If a parish could grow oats, but not wheat, which applies to many in Scotland, then the people ate oatmeal, instead of wheat flour. If the parish could grow barley and apples, but not grapes, then its people drank beer and cider, but not wine. But every parish could grow some kind of cereal and so eat bread; raise some kind of animals and so eat meat; plant some kind of fruit trees and so eat fruit and make drink. Everywhere, people found stone under their feet to build with, or clay to make bricks, or timber growing on their own soil for beams and planks. Fats, in their diet, were local; in the north men used lard, from their pigs, or butter, from their cows. In the south they used neither, but had olive oil. Northern and western men were clothed in the wool of their own sheep; southern men in the cotton of their plantations; eastern men in the silk of their worms.

The point to seize is this: that each very small district, with its own villages and perhaps a town or two, was absolutely self-supporting. Its people depended on nothing and nobody but their own resources and their own work for the essentials of life. They built with their own stone, worked out many of their own techniques, were fed and clothed off their own farms, wore shoes of the hides of their own cattle. Since almost every parish lacked something necessary to the maintenance of that standard of living which was the norm for the whole community, certain things had to be bought abroad—that is, from some near parish. There were trades, such as iron-working, which were specialized in certain places. But there was no difficulty about this, because most parishes could produce a surplus of something wanted elsewhere. This surplus paid for the things needed from outside the parish. Those parishes which had little or nothing to offer remained poor in goods and amenities, but even so did not starve or go naked. Those parishes which were rich in resources were able to raise their standards, to buy from beyond their economic boundaries such things as iron-work, exotic foods and drinks such as oranges and wine, exotic fabrics such as silk, and nourishment for the spirit such as books and paintings, and the services of priests, doctors and lawyers.

What did such a system mean in practice? It meant that no parish in the western system of civilization could starve merely because communications broke down. They did not depend on communications or trade or barter for the means of subsistence. Any small area of, for example, Britain, could and did feed and clothe its own people off its own soil without importing any necessity from the next parish, much less from overseas. It was not an easy life; a bad harvest might cause famine, and even a good one called for hard work. But it was a life which was free from the humiliations of dependence, at least in theory. And it was such a system which produced the Europe of the Renaissance; it produced Shakespeare and Milton, Racine and Corneille, Rembrandt and Newton and Bach and Erasmus. In short, it produced such surpluses as would support a high culture, but which would not support parasitic commercial cities of enormous size.

It is not, however, our purpose to examine this system in detail, nor to argue for or against it. We are concerned to establish only one simple fact: that in those days and under the system whereby a man ate and wore what he grew and made with his own hands, nobody could starve or go naked excepting where harvests failed totally year after year; or where the cities, with their kings and armies, living parasitically off the country-side, robbed the farmers of more than a reasonable part of their produce by taxation backed by armed force, as happened in the France of the *Ancien Régime*.

Under such a system, first things were put first, so that about 80% or more of the population everywhere was occupied in tilling land or raising stock for its own needs and such surpluses as it could get out of the resources available. In those days a man ate the bread his wife had baked from the wheat he had grown, and the exceptions to this rule were few. Who were they? They were of two kinds. The rural craftsmen who specialized in, for example, mason's work, carpentry, pottery, thatching, dyeing, fulling cloth, blacksmithing. In return for the necessary and admirable work which they did, these secondary producers were paid by the primary producers, the farmers. The second non-farming group were really of the same order, but they were further removed from immediate contact with the soil. They were the city folk, and the services they rendered were government, soldiering, merchanting—that is, trade—painting, writing and composing music, praying in the churches and temples. For such services these urban secondary producers were paid by the farmers' surplus production, though for convenience money was used, as rents or as taxes and rates.

Now, such a society as this had certain great advantages. You can see for yourself that it was very stable and well-balanced. Far more people were engaged in producing the raw material of life than in any other occupation. After them, a second large number were engaged in working this material up into the desired form—as food, as furniture, as tools, as poems, as philosophical systems. A much smaller body of people was engaged in administering and organizing the work of the rest. And a few, the adventurous, the unstable members of society, the misfits, did the dirty work of fighting, led by aristocrats whose business that was, and who were, unfortunately, able to extort far more than their fair share of the general wealth, because they controlled the armed forces of the community. Think of this society as a factory. It is a pyramid: at the base, very broad, are thousands of workers, the actual producers; next, not so numerous—and therefore the pyramid narrows—the secondary, highly skilled fitters and pattern-makers; next, fewer again, the office staff of those organizing the work; and, finally, the board of directors as the government, with the managing director, the king, as the peak of the pyramid. Such a figure is stable and hard to overturn. Such a system lasted a thousand years. It would have lasted longer still if the men on top, the aristocrats, and the merchants, with their parasites the lawyers, had been able to restrain themselves from grabbing more than a fair share of the common wealth, and so destroying the system from the bottom.

Our analogue of a factory is misleading in some ways, for the fine thing about this system at its best was that the produce of the men at the base belonged to them. They, in the last analysis, were the bosses. Just as, today, an allotment holder is dependent on nothing but his own hand and brain for a supply of cauliflower in season, so, in those days, every man got his pay for work in the form of consumable produce off his own land, produced by his own hands. Wars only caused famines or shortages in the near neighbourhood of the actual battlefields, and no country, not even islands like Britain, was in the slightest danger of going short of any *essential* material because of something happening in America or Timbuctoo or Wanganui, or because war had closed the seas to shipping.

Such communities as we have described, self-sufficient in every necessary thing, are not only internally, but also externally strong. It was such a *peasant* community, Sparta (though with ugly modifications), that destroyed Athens, a country which could not feed herself off her own soil and depended on trade overseas, on exports. It was such a *peasant* community, the Rome of the Republic, that destroyed trading and exporting Carthage; it was such a *peasant* community, Tudor England, that destroyed the power of Spain, dependent increasingly on American gold and external trade. The enormous strength of France, enabling her to recover from the most crippling defeats, is due to the same cause. As for England, she has survived by reason of her overwhelming sea-power, and, more recently, the ingenuity and technical genius of her people, which keep them ahead in the modern mechanical arts; by reason also of her genius in the modern version of seafaring—merchant and military aviation; and, not least, of her alliance with another self-sufficient and in some respects "peasant" people . . . the Americans.

*

Now let us look at the disadvantages of such a system, in which the great majority of the population is engaged on primary production. Progressive thinkers say something like this: It is true that men can subsist by the means you describe, but they can do little more than that. If so many people are tied to the drudgery of tilling the soil, there will be too few released for the work of forwarding civilization, for science and the arts, philosophy, and the development of the potential genius of man in leisure. Therefore such a system as you describe is reactionary and bad. Moreover, it's inefficient, because it means that everyone is a jack-of-all-trades, has to do a bit of everything more or less well—farm the land, make shift to spin and weave cloth, cobble up a pair of shoes and so forth. For real efficiency it is necessary that men should specialize and so become much more highly skilled than these non-specialist workers could.

There is a lot in this argument: it is an undeniable fact that if a society is to enjoy, for example, the fine arts, certain men must be released from tillage and do nothing but paint or write or make music. But the argument is not so good as it sounds, and we shall list a few facts to prove that this is so; and, to be fair, a few in support of the argument.

1. The most beautiful and enduring work in metal-working has been produced by specialists living and working in close association with their agricultural communities, not in factories.

2. The most beautiful and useful pottery was produced, whether in the ancient or modern worlds, by small or smallish workshops of specialists, also closely associated with agricultural communities.

3. Lace, perhaps the most exquisite of the fine crafts, was a cottage industry.

4. The fine cloths woven by hand and with the most primitive tools by the Inca women have *never been equalled.* These women were the wives of peasant cultivators.

5. Every great artistic culture has risen out of a peasant community.

But—

6. It is inconceivable that an aeroplane engine or a surgeon's scalpel could be produced in anything but a highly scientific, anti-rural urban factory served by laboratories.

7. All modern science demands specialization of an extreme type. None of the arts do so.

Something emerges from this kind of list, which the reader is invited to prolong for himself. Namely, if you want a highly scientific society, then specialization is essential; if you want an artistic society, then only a very moderate degree of specialization is necessary. But it is always true that *some* men must be released from farming duty, and allowed to work their own way.

How did specialization come into being? It has always been a difficult problem to fit the specialist into very stable societies. In the most stable of all, that of pre-conquest Peru, it was done by the craftsman's neighbours cultivating his bit of land for him and keeping the produce for his use. But in the west there has never been so rigid an order. In our societies, specialization was not allowed for and planned: it "just growed". There are examples of it very early indeed. Flint-mining, for example, was a specialized trade in the Old Stone Age, the miners exchanging their flint or their knapped flint tools and weapons for food. Potters and weavers were not, at first, specialists; they worked, as it were, in their spare time, at these trades. But smithing was a specialist trade from the start. What happens is something like this: a whole community wants, let us say, coal. One of its parishes has coal under its soil, but its people, who have their food and clothing to grow and make, have no time to dig up more than they can use for themselves. So the other parishes say, as it were: Look, you stop ploughing and minding sheep and reaping, and concentrate on digging coal. Send us all the coal we want, and, in return, we will grow more wheat and keep more sheep so as to have a surplus to send you in exchange. Then we shall all be better off, because we shall have everything we had before, and coal also.

That, in the very crudest terms, is the case of primary non-agricultural production, like mining and fishing. Then there is secondary specialization. Let us suppose there is a genius in a parish who finds out a superior way of hardening iron and so makes better knives and ploughshares than anyone else has. Some of his fellow parishioners helping him, he makes knives and ploughshares for the whole parish, and receives his food and clothing in exchange, and even rather more than his fair share because he is a public benefactor, or, if you prefer it, because his goods are so much in demand that he can blackmail his fellow parishioners into making a great man of him. Visitors from other parishes see the superior knives and ploughshares, and want them. They offer their own surpluses in exchange, and gradually the whole of the parish abandons agriculture and takes to iron-working, selling its knives in exchange for food and clothing, and, like the first inventor, extorting more than they would be able to grow for themselves. This is the beginning of industrial riches by specialization; and the beginning of the rot which is now destroying us. The non-agricultural parishes become richer in essentials, by trade, than the primary producer parishes, although the former grow nothing for themselves.

In its early stages this specialization did not, in any important particular, transcend national frontiers. Within those frontiers, the independence of regions, of parishes, vanished. Here and there throughout the nation were communities no longer engaged in growing their own necessities, but in working at special trades—iron, pottery, furniture making and so forth, and receiving food from other parishes in return for these goods. Even in those days, however, this system showed flaws. In a bad harvest, the farmers kept what there was, of course, unless it was forced out of them, and the secondary workers went without. Still, civilization was enormously advanced by this modification of the original intensely local system because there was a far wider distribution of all kinds of local goods, and people who could only grow oats could still eat wheat, people who had no clay could still have pots, people who had no iron could have tools, and people who lived inland could eat fish. As an extension of the same change, more and more men could be released from immediate concern with tillage, and could paint and write, and build beautiful palaces and churches. In short, the surpluses were used to increase the standard of living, and as people found that they wanted this higher standard they worked harder and invented new ways of increasing these surpluses. There are many moralists who believe that this constant creation of new needs, new wants, is wicked. Up to a point it is nothing of the sort—it is admirable. It becomes wicked when the need itself is pernicious. When, for example, genius created a need for great buildings, music or poetry, something noble was added to man; but when rapacity creates a new need for tobacco or coco-cola or pornographic, sado-masochist "comics", then this is wicked indeed.

In addition to the exchange of commodities inside the nation, there was, from a very early date, foreign trade. But we ought to be very clear as to the nature of this trade, the sort of goods it dealt in. They were luxuries. Long before the Romanisation of Britain, the Belgic upper classes in the south of England were importing such luxuries as wine into their country. But the cessation of this trade would have hurt nobody, and it is equally true that for nearly two thousand years, in fact until little more than a century ago, nobody in Britain would have starved had all foreign trade come to an end. This by no means implies that we believe that foreign trade is a bad thing: on the contrary, it is admirable and desirable for just so long as it does not cost the people engaged in it their independence.

Where, then, are we to draw the line? If Britain, as a nation, is not to be dependent on foreign sources for food, why, in logic, should the Welsh coalfields or the Lancashire cotton mills be dependent on Kent or Devonshire for their food? Once the question is put, the answer is obvious. It would be ideal if the trust and mutual esteem which holds together the citizens within one nation extended to the whole world, and if the system of free trade which operates within national frontiers covered the whole world. But, in fact, neither of these things are true. We would therefore propose, as an axiom, that the largest unit within which it is safe to have a system of exchange involving not only secondary goods but primary foodstuffs and raw materials, is that unit within which the people identify the interests of the community with their own interests. It happens that today that unit is the nation. A case could be made out to show that it is, for us, the Commonwealth; but as the member nations of that group are scattered, as therefore Britain can be isolated from the others by hostile sea and air craft and we may be confined within our own island, it is not safe to depend on the Commonwealth. It is conceivable that food supplies might easily fail from Europe, from the Commonwealth, or from America, either because we could no longer pay for them; or because these countries have no longer any surplus to send; or because a state of war closes the sea- and air-ways. In fact, all these things have happened and are happening. But it is hardly likely that Kent will refuse to send apples to Manchester or Devon milk to Wales, because cotton or coal are not required. Occasionally something like this does, in fact, happen; but it is due to the anomalies of our system of distribution, not to any fundamental failure of demand.

We have, in our argument, reached this point: that we must produce sufficient of the basic materials for living, for all our population, off our own land, not on principle, but because:

(*a*) We no longer have the means to buy them overseas.

(*b*) Even if we had, we have had too bitter experiences of what this dependence means.

(*c*) It is criminal folly not to develop our two greatest assets, the quality of our people and the fertility of our soil, to the utmost.

(*d*) Overseas countries have less and less, surplus to their own needs, to send us.

(*e*) War, in which submarines and aircraft are used as commerce-destroyers, puts us at the mercy of our enemy even for our bread and meat.

To return to our explanation:

Britain was the first country to break free of the system whereby each small, geographical unit was self-supporting.

The first phase of this great change was the Agricultural Revolution. In the course of it the land was taken away from the people, its owners, enclosed, cultivated by new methods devised by a series of men of genius, and was thus worked at a much higher standard of *economic* efficiency. By this we mean that yields of all crops were raised while the size and other attributes of the crops were improved. The size and quality of cattle, sheep and horses were improved. Farm building and planning were improved. Soil fertility was built up. Englishmen, in short, invented a system of good farming which taught the whole world. But here we are going to introduce a new term: we are going to contrast economic efficiency with *social* efficiency. Economic efficiency is concerned with the quantity of food produced per acre; with the skill and organization whereby more production is obtained for less work, calculated in man-hours. It is based on the idea that there are not enough hands to do the world's work, but that there are too many mouths to eat the product of that work: now here, surely, there is an inconsistency; there are two hands for every mouth in the world. And this reveals to us that the worship of economic efficiency is based upon a very noble idea: it is designed for a world in which there is free trade and mutual love operating over the whole surface of the earth, so that the products of every man's work are available to every other man in the world. And it is also based upon the idea that if we can constantly reduce the amount and weight of physical work which must be done in order that we shall eat, be clothed, and be housed in comfort and dignity . . . all of us, every man, woman and child in the world, then men will be released from drudgery and be able to develop the spirit, to practice philosophy, the arts, the sciences and religion.

Such was the great liberal vision of the nineteenth-century

thinkers, and out of it rises the notion of economic efficiency as a desirable objective.

But what are the facts about our world? Trade is much less free than it was formerly. There is less love and trust between nations than there was a century ago. The soil has proved not to be inexhaustible, as it was supposed to be. Hardly any of the conditions exist in which a system of high economic efficiency can operate properly, with the result that this kind of efficiency has resulted in the most frightful disasters . . . in the helpless dependence of millions and millions of office and factory specialist workers upon remote and indifferent peoples for their food and clothing, the sources of which are shrinking instead of expanding.

Now, what do we mean by social efficiency, as opposed to economic efficiency? We mean by this a system which does not produce more and more goods for less and less labour, regardless of the happiness and well-being of the producers and consumers, and as an end in itself, but one which makes for the optimum of economic efficiency while providing the optimum of basic security and of congenial labour. We would say something like this: if men can eat oranges, apples and bananas at the cost of having to do work of no interest, with no creative satisfaction, in factory slums, and become bored, mentally and morally slack, and spiritually bankrupt in the process; and if they have to give up the oranges and bananas, and make do with apples only, as the price of giving up the factory slum and growing their own apples, finding the work interesting and being morally, mentally and spiritually braced in the process, then for God's sake let them adopt the second alternative.

Even if it were always and absolutely true that a few specialists working a few machines are more economically efficient than a large number of peasants or craftsmen producing the same amount of goods with their hands, we ought still to ask ourselves: which is the more *socially* efficient? Which system will give the people more security in essential products, will keep them more absorbed in their work, will give them more satisfaction and more purpose and will enable them to express themselves better as men, not as labour-units? And we know the answer. Socially, industrialism is a dismal and hideous failure. Let us face that fact. And that it may be economically efficient is of absolutely no interest in the world as we have made it: men are not made for ways of life, but ways of life for men.

Now, under the old system whereby the people got their food and clothing by working with soil and animals, economic efficiency was low, but social efficiency was high. That is why the men of this system accumulated such terrific energy and showed such tremendous inventive initiative and such admirable taste in the applied and fine arts, in religion and philosophy and science. Their very progress in these fully human adult activities destroyed the system which made them possible. There is a kind of freedom ignored by politicians, which is precious: it is the freedom of the Jolly Miller who sang that he cared for nobody, no, not he, and nobody cared for him. It is the freedom of a man who is bound to toil on his bit of land, but is not bound to anything or anyone else. The peasant had this freedom, and when some progress had been made in the art and science of agriculture, he could extend it, he could have surpluses to sell, he could enlarge his economic as well as his moral freedom.

Under the system created by the Agricultural Revolution, this kind of subsistence-and-surpluses farming disappeared, and "cash-crop farming" took its place. As a result, neither man nor parish made any attempt to grow all that was locally needed. Specialization came in, a few things were cultivated, suited to the region, and these were sold for money, with which necessities and luxuries could be bought outside the parish, the county, the nation. But here, right from the start, was a major flaw in the new system: only a few benefited from it. Men who had been land-holding peasants dependent on nothing but their hands for their subsistence, became landless labourers, with no rights, dependent upon the goodwill of an employer, for a job, wages, and so, subsistence. Social freedom was lost by the many, in order that an unprecedented economic freedom might be gained by the few.

Let us be quite clear that there was no intention on the part of the makers of the Agricultural Revolution that men should starve in order that a few might be much richer than before. It was believed that if, by a rational and economic management of the land, the national production of crops could be greatly increased, then the increase in national wealth would be such that the dispossessed peasants would gain, as employed workers with high wages, far more than they had lost. The fact that they were paid in money instead of in kind for their work, would mean that they would gain immensely in economic freedom: instead of being confined to the barley they could grow, they would have the choice of the wheat or oats which other men grew, and so forth. To some extent this was true; its originators were not to know that it would break down, their lovely flexible, liberal system, against human nature itself. Themselves supremely rational, they supposed that all men would and could become so. They were mistaken.

The price of economic freedom, in the world as we have it, is insecurity. The price of security in essential food and materials, is agricultural nationalism. This is a bad thing. But it is *so*. We must try to alter it; meanwhile, let us recognize it rather than starve to death.

*

Before going on to the next part of this review, there is one thing to be said. With modern means, it can be shown that, on some land, small-scale farming is, as it happens, economically as well as socially *more* efficient than large-scale "industrial" farming.

Britain's next step along the road to world leadership and ruin was the Industrial Revolution. You know all about that. We built and manned more and more factories as we found more and more foreign peoples ready and willing to buy our manufactured goods in exchange for their raw materials and their food. In the process of herding factory workers together in factories and in mines, the population increased to five or six times what it had been. When it was about 20 million, the marvellously efficient and productive system of agriculture which we had evolved or invented, enabled us to feed ourselves still off our own land. It might have been possible to feed even a larger population off that land, but the cost of the so-called "high" farming which could do this was very great. In order to do it, a relatively small area of soil had to be made to produce enormous crops. This could be done, but it was costly. What alternative was there? That of buying food abroad, from countries with vast undeveloped territories, whose stores of soil fertility had never been broached. This was actually done. Why? For a very ignoble reason—the greed and rapacity of the great industrialists. Or, if you like, their blind submission to what Adam Smith had told them were immutable economic "laws". These men wanted to pay their factory hands the lowest possible wage, so that their goods would be cheap, and so sell easily, while still bringing in large profits. But they realized that since even factory hands must eat, if wages were to be low, then food prices must be low. But the English farmer could not supply enough food at a low price. So they went elsewhere, imported food, and drove the English farmer to reduce his standards of farming, to work his land not as *productively* as possible, but as *cheaply* as possible.

Why was the food from overseas so cheap? For two main reasons: either it came from the great new countries where the farmers could cash in on the accumulated fertility of the soil by growing crops on it until it was exhausted, and then moving on to new virgin soil, thus getting crops without manure and with very little work. Or this imported food came from countries where a powerful ruling class held a miserable peasantry in thrall, and could simply take their home-grown food away from them and sell it to the English and other Europeans who were copying the English; or change food crops, such as wheat, for industrial crops, such as cotton, in return for goods which the rulers kept for their own class. Hence the continuance in miserable poverty of the Egyptian *fellahin*, the Indian *ryats*, and other peasant peoples.

So the industrial prosperity, financial supremacy and scientific leadership of Great Britain was won not only by the energy and ingenuity of Englishmen, but by the dispossession of English peasants, the ruin of English farming, the spoliation of the new soils of America and Australia and other countries, the suffering and agony of Indian and Egyptian and African peasants. It is an ugly story; and none of it need have happened if social efficiency had been put before economic efficiency.

*

There then appeared a new idea: socialism. The socialist said in effect: "*Economic and social efficiency can be combined.* This system, whereby men are not confined to consuming the goods and services which the land they stand on will yield, but, by specialization and exchange, can enjoy the whole world, is admirable. The only thing wrong with industrial capitalism is that the actual producers, the workers, are deprived by the master men of its benefits. Let the workers take over the system and run it, through the State, for the benefit of all instead of for that of a few, and *then* we shall have the kind of world which men deserve."

And just as it seemed that by some such method as this it would be possible for all men to enjoy the whole world and its fruits by a system combining social with economic efficiency, things began to go wrong, especially for the English. What were, and are, these things?

1. Certain countries, notably the U.S.A. and the U.S.S.R., have within their own frontiers all the resources which a full development of civilization requires. Their period of expansion is coming to an end: their period of stabilization is beginning. They have no real need to buy manufactured goods, and

relatively insignificant requirements in the way of raw materials from oversea. Their imports are increasingly of non-essentials, luxuries. Consequently, we, the British, have little to offer in exchange for food and raw materials, excepting the products of our science and arts—jet engines, whisky, novels.

2. Even if we, the British, had enough goods to offer which were really wanted in the self-sufficient countries, they, on their part, have less and less surplus to sell. There are two reasons for this: their home consumption is rising as their populations and standards of living increase; their production of agricultural goods is either falling or not rising in step with their own increasing consumption, because of the exhaustion of soil which was cashed for capital goods in the 19th century.

3. We, the British, now number 50 millions. Our potential agricultural land amounts to:

Arable	16,869,000 acres
Permanent pasture . . .	11,990,000 ,,
Leys (temporary pastures) .	5,274,000 ,,
Rough pasture . . .	16,356,000 ,,
Orchards	287,000 ,,

In all, about 50 million acres of land capable of producing food of some kind, if we include 10 or 12 million acres of marginal land which is not being used at all, but which could be used. *But* it takes about two acres of land to feed a man, let alone clothe him. In short, at the present level of farming efficiency and by present methods, it is impossible to feed and clothe more than about 40% of our population off our own soil.

4. Formerly there were countries willing to specialize in growing food and to import their manufactured goods in exchange for it. But Britain's forced failure to maintain supplies of manufactures, during two world wars drove these agrarian peoples to build their own factories. This was in keeping with the rising spirit of nationalism; and now they

wish to be industrially self-supporting. Thus they are no longer anxious, or even *willing* food-exporters.

5. Where the Old World was concerned, Britain's food and raw material importers dealt, in the past, with the master men abroad who, in many food-exporting countries, were holding down a peasantry in misery, for their own profit. The food grown by this peasantry was sold to Britain without the consent of the growers, and against their interests. Or food crops gave way to industrial crops, as in Egypt. The change of political régimes in those countries has meant in many cases the cessation of these forced exports.

6. The progress of very ancient soil erosion and exhaustion in such countries as India and China, and of very new soil erosion and exhaustion in such countries as Africa and Australia, is having a twofold effect: it is forcing even agrarian countries to import food; and it is making exports of food in the fewer and fewer good harvest years very unwise. Thus, this source of foreign foodstuffs is also drying up.

7. At least two other countries, and probably more, are in much the same situation as Great Britain: Germany and Japan are both seriously overpopulated in relation to their food-growing capacity and must import food by exporting manufactured goods. Whereas Britain is politically progressive and must pay higher and higher wages, both these countries are politically reactionary and can pay low wages. Furthermore, whereas Britain, although an American ally, is still regarded as fully independent and must stand on her own feet, Western Germany is the geographical site of the United States front line against the U.S.S.R. and must therefore be maintained with food supplies by her patron, while Eastern Germany is the U.S.S.R.'s front line against the U.S.A. and must be similarly assisted and is, in any case, agrarian. Japan has become an American colony in everything but name and appearance. Thus Britain is not in an easy position to compete with these two semi-colonial regions in the world's export markets; especially as the rising nationalist and racial feeling

in such countries as India tend to make them buy from an Asiatic rather than a European source.

8. Food sources in the U.S.S.R. and other Communist countries are put out of bounds by political considerations, and, in any case, would never be reliable owing to the expanding populations and rising standards in those countries, which mean rising home consumption.

*

To sum up: it is *apparently* impossible for us to feed more than half our population off our own soil.

Our erstwhile foreign suppliers either cannot continue to send us food because they have not got it to spare.

Or they will not continue to send food because they have no demand for what we can manage to send them in exchange.

On the basis of these three simple truths, we will shortly, once expedients and evasions come to an end, starve.

But things are not quite so bad as that. In the next chapter we "go into the figures". As we cannot make statistics exciting, we have tried to make them clear. These figures will establish that we have been writing sense. When we have disposed of them we will come to the brighter side of the picture.

CHAPTER II

What We Eat and Where It Comes From

We do not propose, in this chapter, to go into details, but rather to give the massive figures and facts as simply and clearly as possible. The figures are not accurate to a few tons: there is no need for them to be so, nor would it be possible to give them exactly. But they are accurate within a few hundreds of tons, and since the totals in question are counted in millions of tons, the approximation is so close that the argument dependent upon it is unaffected by minor errors.

BREAD

We have headed this section "bread" because of the ancient and moving associations of the word: more exactly, we should have written "wheat", for it is with all the foods made from wheaten flour that we are here concerned. As to how that flour is used, the careless destruction of part of its food value before it reaches us as a loaf of bread, that is a subject which we deal with in its place.

The people of Britain consume about two hundredweight of wheat per head every year. The total figure for 1950, for example, was 5,453,000 tons. In the same year British farmers grew and harvested 1,595,000 tons of wheat. The remainder was obtained from overseas, as follows:

From Australia	353,000 tons
,, Canada	2,947,000 ,,
,, U.S.A.	499,000 ,,
,, other sources . . .	59,000 ,,

What do these figures mean to the individual Briton? That every time he eats a loaf of bread only about one-third of it comes from farmers who belong to a community with which both consumer and producer identify their interests. Canada, supplying more than a half of our loaf, is our friend and close relation: but she is separated from us by thousands of miles of ocean, she has a soil exhaustion and erosion problem, she has a growing population, and its needs in manufactured goods are more easily and immediately supplied by her near neighbour and friend, the United States. Moreover, Great Britain is already very heavily in Canada's debt, so that every ton of wheat we receive from her is supplied on credit.

Australia has already been forced to reduce her imports from Britain. She has not the means to pay for them, nor can Britain always supply her industrial needs as exactly and promptly as can the United States. Australia's agrarian economy is constantly being disturbed by droughts of long duration. Her soil erosion and exhaustion problem is immediate and terrible. Her grazing ranges have been overstocked, they need water, they are infested with rabbits and with dingoes.

Of the United States' soil problem, nothing need be said: the Dust Bowl story is well known, and much has been done in the U.S. to conserve and rehabilitate soil fertility. Nevertheless, the country is still forced, for reasons which are not economic but political, to export soil fertility. In the interests of her own people and of her future, she will have to stop doing this soon rather than later. So little need has she of those manufactured goods which we can export, and with which we might pay for wheat, that, in fact, very little of that wheat is paid for with British goods: it is paid for with such raw materials as rubber and tin, which come from Malaya and other colonies, which we now control virtually by force. We are able to pay America a small part of what we constantly owe her—the fraction which we *can* pay—by exploiting certain of our colonial territories and their sullen populations; for it is very doubtful whether we put back into those territories nearly as much as we get out of them.

What can we conclude from these facts and figures? How

many of the twenty slices into which we cut our daily loaf really belong to us, are paid for, not given or lent; are, in short, secure tomorrow as well as today? *About seven slices.*

OATS AND BARLEY

Although we eat these other cereals, they are more important as animal foods; that is, we eat them indirectly as meat. And barley, of course, makes our beer. In 1950 we consumed 2,707,000 tons of oats, and, in the same year, our farmers grew and harvested 2,617,000 tons. The year taken is representative. In short, 97% of our oats are home-grown, and only 3% imported, so that the situation in regard to this cereal is very satisfactory, excepting that we could do with more.

The case of barley is more difficult to present because it seems that we buy it here and there at random, finding new sources of supply each year and losing old ones. Of the 2,359,000 tons consumed in 1950 by ourselves, our cattle and our brewers, we grew at home 68%. For the rest, we went to Iraq for 146,000 tons, hardly a reliable source of supply for the future; 324,000 tons came from the U.S.S.R., which country sells foodstuffs as a political, not as an economic act, and so cannot be depended upon for more than the term of a one-year agreement. When trading with the U.S.S.R. and the U.S.A., we are not, for more than a small fraction of the total, undertaking a mutually beneficial social act, but simply taking advantage of some ephemeral political mood. From numerous other foreign sources we bought a further 294,000 tons of barley.

How many pints of beer shall we do without if we cannot buy foreign barley? Three out of ten. How many of our pigs may die in the same case? Thirty-two out of every 100.

*

It is sufficiently clear that in the matter of the three great cereal foods about one-half of our necessary supplies come to us from sources which, for one or more of the reasons sketched in Chapter I, are not reliable and cannot, in the nature of things today, be so. It is equally clear that unless we take remedial action any one or more of numerous causes can result in half our population going without bread; or all of it without half the cereal foods which we eat today, in which bacon must be included, for it is in bacon that we eat barley.

OILS AND FATS

Not even the most austere moralist could accuse the British people of eating too much fat today. Our consumption of fats is probably as low as it ought to be, and is kept low by the very small rations of butter, margarine, lard, cooking fat; and by the very high price of olive oil and of inferior edible oils, such as ground-nut oil.

For a northern country with rich pasture and the possibility of increasing secondary pasture, the natural fat to eat is a milk derivative—butter, cheese. On the other hand, for countries with a Mediterranean (dry-farming) soil and climate, the natural fat to eat is olive oil. There is no need to insist upon this pattern; and, of course, exchange is a legitimate means of diversifying our diet. But there is a world of difference between exchange, and the desperate expedient of scraping up of bits and pieces of supply, wherever we can get it.

Disregarding butter, we consume about 1,300,000 tons of oils and fats every year. And counting the oil obtained at sea by British whalers, we produce about 175,000 tons, i.e. 13% of our consumption. For the balance, sources of supply and their contributions are:

Argentine	16%
British West Africa	42%
India	1%
Malaya	5%
Numerous small sources	23%

As we all know, the Argentinos from time to time assert their national dignity by cutting off supplies of the foodstuffs they send us. They are separated from us by thousands of miles of ocean open, in war-time, to hostile submarines, and of sky open to hostile aircraft. Moreover, there is no reason to assume that they will always be on "our" side; why should they? The British West African source has a serious soil problem, an equally serious problem in the disease affecting oil plants. It has other disadvantages, apart from the obvious geographical one: its people are seething with new nationalism, and Britain may be driven to exacerbate these feelings and give them a definitely anti-British bias, by paying too much deference to the anti-Negro superstitions of the South African Boers. India is already a food-importing, half-starved country, suffering from over-population, a disastrously high birth-rate and a death-rate too low for her exhausted soil to support. It would be absurd ever again to regard India as a source of any food whatsoever; she must, on the contrary, be regarded as a competitor in the world's food markets. There is also a moral aspect to this problem: every time an Englishman eats rice, he is helping to starve an Indian from whom English medical science has withdrawn the blessed mercy of death. Could any statement be more illiberal than this? Yet it is true; it is the condition brought about by the partnership between science and industrialism, the latter corrupted by greed, the former by a want of philosophical guidance. Indian food-production can and will rise, but not nearly fast enough.

Malaya is an unsatisfactory source of food or of anything else, for she has to be held down by armed force. Suppose this force to be withdrawn? Can we depend on being able to trade with the Malays? Probably we can, but not as owners of their rubber and food plantations, able to ship their oil and their other products to our own and to United States ports, at our pleasure.

How much of the weekly 8 ounces of fats and oils which we, each of us, eat, can be counted on, can be regarded as safe, will be there tomorrow? *About 2 ounces.*

In addition to these fats and oils, we each eat about 3 ounces of butter every week. Our total national consumption is about 300,000 tons a year. Of this we produce at home 25,000 tons. Sources of supply of 93% of our butter—all but a teaspoonful per head per week—are Australia, New Zealand, Denmark and the Netherlands. Denmark is close and friendly and we might regard about 50% of our need as secure, since 35% comes from there. The Netherlands, too, are satisfactory as butter-suppliers. The Dominions are too far from us and increasingly independent of our industry.

OTHER MILK PRODUCTS

Of approximately 75,000 tons of dried milk consumed annually, we produce at home 41,000 tons and buy 34,000 tons from Australia, New Zealand, Holland and others. We buy only 27,000 tons of condensed milk abroad and produce 141,000 tons at home. Of the 200,000 tons of cheese we eat every year, 150,000 tons are imported and 50,000 tons made in Britain. Forty per cent. of the total comes from New Zealand, 12,000 miles away.

BACON AND HAM

Of bacon and ham in all forms we ate 20 lb. per head in 1950: 474,000 tons in all. Where did the 20 lb. each come from? About 8 lb. from home farms, and the other 12 lb. from Denmark (30%), the Netherlands, Canada, Poland, Eire and other countries. The pattern is changing. Poland is not a regular supplier, and our own production is rising. Distant sources suffer from the usual disability. In any case, the total annual consumption falls short of need, which would probably be of the order of 40 lb. per head if we really enjoyed that high standard of living which the politicians and journalists are always threatening to take away from us.

We can probably regard as secure about a quarter of a pound of bacon and ham every week each, consumed at home, in restaurants and in canteens. We are not likely to grow very fat on that.

MEAT

The case of meat is complicated by the difficulty of ascertaining to what extent "home-produced" meat is really home-fed. We do actually produce more than half our annual meat consumption on our own farms. (In 1950: imports, 848,000 tons; home-fed, 903,000 tons.) Setting aside the fact that we may regard the weekly meat-ration as inadequate, which is questionable, for we are a healthy and vigorous people on our present rations, let us consider how that ration is supplied.

We dare not regard as really home-grown, livestock which is fed on imported foods. Apart from the large imports of barley, we bring in annually about 1 million tons of maize, nearly all of it by temporary expedients of no long-term significance—for example, by agreements with the U.S.S.R. lasting for one or two years. We also import about 450,000 tons of oil-cake for feeding cattle, and manufacture a further 681,000 tons from imported oil seeds. One per cent. of the domestic manufacture of oil-cake is made from home-grown oil seeds.

But a relatively small proportion of imported, or partly imported cattle food is fed to beasts intended for meat, and consequently it is fairly safe to say that about half our meat supply really is home-grown. In 1950 we ate 1,751,000 tons of carcase meat and offal. Although the meat ration is probably not inadequate, it certainly would be if it had to be cut by half, and since very little of our imported meat can be regarded as safe, our problem is to double the home production.

It is quite possible for a nation to be vegetarian and flourish: the ancient Athenians lived largely on wheat and olive oil, ceasing to be meat-eaters because their population was far too large for their home farm resources. The mighty and orderly civilization of the Incas was built on a diet of maize, not meat.

Meat, especially beef, is an "uneconomic" way of using land, of converting soil fertility into human food, if we consider simply food values, the food value of a beef carcase against that of the wheat or barley which could have been grown on the land required to fatten the bullock. The problem is often looked at from that point of view. But it is very bad farming to value a beast simply as so much meat. To grow good cereal crops, animal manure is better and cheaper than industrial fertilizers. It is proper and wise to attribute some part of our cereal crop to the fat cattle which were fed off the land before wheat or barley were planted in it. To some extent a crop of cereal or vegetables or fruit is due to the animal dung with which the field or orchard was dressed. Manure from milch cattle, unless fed largely on concentrates, is inferior to manure from beef cattle because we take from the cow far more soil nutrients, as part of the milk, than we take from the steer as meat. For much the same reason, beef cattle take less out of pasture than do milch cattle.

All things considered, although one of the shortest cuts to national independence in the matter of food would be that of turning vegetarian, we are justified in planning to double our meat production, perhaps with the emphasis on sheep rather than cattle, in order to maintain the existing meat ration while rendering ourselves independent of:

Argentine	13% of our meat
Australia	7% ,, ,, ,,
New Zealand . . .	21% ,, ,, ,,
Other sources . . .	7% ,, ,, ,,

Let us suppose that we succeed: this by no means entails the wanton ruining of our relatives in the Dominions. We should be in a position to increase our meat consumption by so much as we could pay for out of genuinely needed exports. We should be willing to accept meat in payment for motor-cars or jet aircraft. But we should not have to go on buying meat on tick.

One source of oversea supply is very unsatisfactory: the Argentine. Ignoring such differences in economic and political matters as estrange us, from time to time, from that country, there are other reasons against depending on the Argentine for meat. The Republic has a rising population; it has a falling soil fertility; its ranges have been overstocked and will have to be rested if they are not to be ruined; industrialism is on the increase, as always happens when nationalism becomes the policy of a once-agrarian country. Here again, however well we were doing off our home farms, we could always accept meat from the Argentine in payment for such of our manufactured goods as she genuinely wanted to buy. But to be dependent on her is folly.

More than a quarter of our meat comes from the Australasian Dominions. Australia is not a satisfactory source of supply, her difficult climate and terrible soil problem are against her and she may have her work cut out to support her own population, let alone ours. New Zealand has a propitious climate and a healthy soil, and she is our best friend; but she is still 12,000 miles away.

In addition to carcase meat and offal, we consume annually about 50,000 tons of corned meat, all imported, some of it from Uruguay and Paraguay as well as the Dominions, the United States (but not now), and Argentine. Other kinds of canned meat are imported from South America, the United States and various countries in Europe. It is probable that we could forego the whole of this annual 5 lb. per head—only an ounce and a half per week—without suffering. But to do so would upset our stock-piling and other contingency supplies.

FISH

Although there have sometimes been small imports of fresh fish, we catch in practice all that we need, or at least all that we consume. Probably we could both catch and eat a good deal more fish, although there are practical difficulties. The principal limiting factor is that the overfishing of certain waters reduces the fish population below that point from which it can easily recover its numbers.

Of the fish caught annually by our fishermen, large quantities are used in the manufacture of fish meals for animal food and for manure, and 16,000 tons, or thereabouts, are canned. Before the war we ate annually about 80,000 tons of canned fish, but the figure is now about half as much. Even so, we are dependent on foreign sources for about 30,000 tons annually, sources of supply being various: Japan, Canada, Norway, Morocco, Portugal, South Africa and the U.S.S.R. Some part of this import is justifiable on the grounds that the product is the speciality of the exporting country—Portuguese sardines in olive oil, for example. These should come under the heading "luxuries"; that is not a reason for refusing to import them, provided we can pay for them with exports. The policy of importing commonplace canned fish is otherwise absurd. There is no shortage of British-caught fish for canning. There is a shortage of tin-plate. Why? Because we export it, and then, presumably, reimport it with foreign fish and foreign fruit in it, while our own fishing industry is working short hours and our fruit-growers are letting their surplus crops rot.

EGGS

As everyone knows, the annual ration of eggs is inadequate. In 1950 we ate 631,000 tons of eggs. In order that eggs could be freely used, as they should, this figure would have to exceed 1 million tons. Home production is about half a million tons a year, but it should be remembered that a large proportion of the food fed to poultry is imported, so that these half-million tons are only partially "home-grown".

From Denmark, Eire and other countries we receive about 100,000 tons of eggs a year.

We produce at home virtually no dried or otherwise preserved eggs, but consume about 20,000 tons, all imported. Or rather, we did; as dried egg came from the U.S., we eat this food no longer. In the households this is no loss, for nobody seemed to like the stuff; but no doubt the stoppage of this import was a serious matter for patent-food manufacturers and food-adulterators generally. We also import, or until recently did import, eggs from China, neither in the shell nor dried, but broken into large cans and sealed. Egg in this form, while far from fresh, can be used by restaurants and canteen kitchens, and makes good omelettes.

There is no doubt whatsoever that we could be self-supporting in eggs; if in 1953 all the eggs produced in Britain were to reach the legal market, we should probably be already well on the way to that happy state. But the price will be high.

FRUIT

The case of fruit is so difficult to present simply, that for figures we have had to substitute a general discussion.

First of all: we could very easily produce in Britain all the fruit we need, other than sub-tropical and tropical kinds. It is quite usual for fruit to be imported, even from hard-currency countries such as the United States and Canada, while home-grown fruit remains unpicked on the trees. The reasons for this criminal folly are several. It is often expedient, politically, for the authorities to import fruit which we do not need; shopkeepers and market dealers seem hostile to all but limited ranges of home fruit produce, partly because the British grower has not the means to pack it in the non-returnable packs which save him trouble; our people are used to having fruit out of season, and so imports of apples, pears and plums at times when they are not in season here are profitable. We are seriously short of apple and pear storage facilities which would enable us to sell the home crop all the year round. The policy of exporting tin-plate and sugar, which could be used to can English fruit, even soft fruit, means in practice that while our own plums and other fruits remain ungathered, foreign plums come to us in English cans and preserved in English sugar. To some extent English growers are also to blame: for example, when there are complaints that farmers cannot sell their cherry crop it will usually be found upon investigation that it is the inferior varieties which remain unbought, and that good cherries always sell. The same is to some extent true of plums.

Before the war we imported as much as 185,000 tons of canned fruit a year, including such semi-exotic fruit as peaches, and such exotics as pineapple. We now import less than a third of that quantity, but much of it is fruit which it is ridiculous to eat out of cans. Most of it comes from Africa and Australia.

We import from Brazil, Italy, Palestine, South Africa and Spain nearly half a million tons of oranges, lemons and grapefruit. These fruits, especially oranges, are said to be particularly valuable in our diet, notably for babies. It is quite certain—we examine this claim in another chapter—that the same qualities could be had from home-grown fruits. The supply of oranges, like that of bananas, can never be regarded as secure; that was demonstrated during the war. Despite the fact that we could easily do without these citrus fruits, there is a strong case for continuing some imports, for food is not merely "diet"; it is also pleasure.

But we should not regard citrus fruit as a necessity.

We import about 150,000 tons, or less, of dried fruit from Australia, Greece, Turkey, Iraq and the U.S.A. Is this import necessary? On the whole, yes. It is evident that we should not starve without it, but here again it is a question of social rather than dietetic values. This is a case where the insecurity of supply is of no importance, however, since dried fruit is not a necessity.

VEGETABLES

The bulk of our vegetables are home grown and *all* of them could be, without any trouble at all. There are seasonal gaps filled by exports from neighbouring countries with slight climatic advantages and a much better organized and more soundly based horticulture. The conditions for making ourselves absolutely independent of imports in the matter of vegetables are: reorganization of distribution on a non-profit basis; capital and labour reinforcement of the industry; paying for vegetables at a price which will make growing them at *the British standard of living for the grower* worth while. We discuss this more fully in Chapter V.

SUGAR

During the 17th-18th centuries sugar was a luxury; before then it was even more so. The habit of eating it was fostered during the 18th and 19th centuries when the sugar plantations of the West Indies and of north-eastern Brazil as well as, later, the eastern colonies of European powers, enriched a few hundreds of merchants and caused the death after untold misery of hundreds of thousands of plantation slaves and indentured labourers. Sugar has the ugliest record of any food material; it is one long, hideous tale of greed, cruelty and rapacity. However, we are now all addicts, and some dieticians can even find good reasons for eating sugar. Others hold it in horror.

The consumption of refined sugar in Britain in 1950 was 2,531,000 tons. Of this vast figure we produce on home farms 554,000 tons. The position, however, is not quite as bad as it looks, for although we imported 1,977,000 tons of sugar, a considerable part of this was not eaten here, but manufactured and re-exported. Sources of sugar supply are:

Australia	9%
British West Indies	11%
Cuba	33%
Dominican Republic	14%
Mauritius	6%
S. Africa	1%
Other sources	4%

This pattern changes from year to year.

TEA

Needless to say, there is no crime in importing tea, since we cannot grow it at home. It is arguable that the rise of the tea-drinking habit among us was a disaster, bringing misery and pain to millions of Indians and Chinese, and indigestion to millions of Europeans. Cobbett and others long pointed out that tea is a dangerous and unwholesome drug, and that to drink it in preference to beer is a sign of national degeneracy. But these reformers were writing and speaking in a time when beer was brewed at home and was certainly very good and wholesome. The Society for the Propagation of Christian Knowledge did its best in the 19th century to put a stop to the socially dangerous and extravagant habit of tea-drinking, and published a book for working-class housewives in which excellent recipes for brewing beer were printed. But to no purpose, and we are today even more completely enslaved to this Oriental drug than we are to the Occidental one on which we also spend millions of our money: tobacco.

Tea comes from India and China, Ceylon and Africa. None of these sources can be regarded as secure, and we may yet have to do without tea. In which case we shall have to increase our barley acreage. Coffee comes into the same class, but is much less important to the British people. However, if war can be avoided, it does happen that the tea-producing countries are exactly those which have real need of the exports of a highly industrialized nation, so that economically we are in a fairly strong position to buy tea at an advantageous price.

*

We can best sum up this chapter by means of a Table, or Balance Sheet (see opposite page), for which purpose we will take the year 1950.

We have described the enormous total of imported food as a deficit with the deliberate intention of emphasizing it. Naturally, we are not suggesting that all food-importing is absolutely foolish and dangerous, and that we must immediately set about putting a stop to it. But the figure is far too large; it was paid for not out of manufactured goods, which we can legitimately offer, but largely out of borrowed money, or by means of raw materials wrung from sullen and rebellious

What We Eat and Where It Comes From

Consumption of Staple Foods in Thousands of Tons		*Home Production of These Same Foods in Thousands of Tons*	
Wheat . . .	5,453		1,595
Other cereals . .	5,066		4,212
Oils and fats . .	1,127		170
Butter . . .	360		25
Preserved milks and cheese . .	451		235
Bacon and ham .	474		215
Meat, in all forms .	1,883		903
Eggs . . .	630		515
		Deficit in staple foods: . .	7,564
	15,444		15,444

colonial peoples who object to seeing their property taken from them and used to feed the British people while they themselves are on very short commons. This is a fact which we ought to face squarely; when the papers rejoice over an enormous sale of Malayan rubber to the United States, what is it that they are celebrating? That we are still strong enough in armed force to continue persuading the Malayans to concur in our domination of their country; not that we are paying our way in the only fashion which has any validity, by the labour and material of our own country. *Labour*, and material. We are not suggesting that goods made from imported raw material which has been fairly paid for are not legitimate articles of trade. Of course they are. But if they have not been paid for and if there is no prospect of paying for them. . . ?

We have been reduced to ugly expedients in order to keep ourselves fed. To a very great extent this has been due to our own failure to make proper use of our own principal asset—our fertile soil and mild climate. What are the facts of this dismal failure? We have already discussed their antecedents. We pass now to the details.

H. J. Massingham

CHAPTER III

The Abuse of Land

OUR GENERATION is confronted with a situation full of paradoxes so extreme as to be barely credible. That we are forced to become a self-supporting nation without more than a small minority of the population being so far aware of it, overtops most of the others. We are compelled to wrench the wheels of our civilization out of its present highway in order to become what our pre-industrial ancestors always were—a people who took it for granted that they should eat what they themselves grew, which is utterly opposed to what our policy, our economics and our philosophy of life have taught us for 150 years. But the situation is even more paradoxical than that. For, whereas our forefathers had only a small population to feed on a much larger acreage than we possess today, we have an enormous one to feed on a much smaller acreage; and the paradox goes on getting worse and worse. Pre-industrial Britain cultivated a food-bearing countryside in much better heart (as the farmers say) than ours is, a land whose natural resources had not been exploited and used up to anything like the extent that ours has been in our time. Even when the New World was discovered, home-production for home-consumption continued to be as inborn a way of life from the 16th to the end of the 18th centuries as it had been to our Stone Age, Bronze Age, Celtic, Saxon and medieval forbears, as normal as riding or driving horses. To us, on the contrary, it is altogether unfamiliar, distasteful, revolutionary, reactionary, eccentric, unthinkable, impossible and abnormal. Our whole society, its education, livelihood and behaviour, its system, ideas and conventions, have conditioned us to accept the exchange of home-manufactures for foreign food-supplies as being as natural to us as the city air we breathe.

Nevertheless, primary facts are not abolished even by millions of people hating or refusing to believe in them. And the primary and fundamental fact is that we must either re-learn how to support ourselves in the near future or perish of famine. It is as appallingly simple as that. More, we deserve that it should be so. Our economic system has been built upon the sand; it has, and had, no justification whether in right, reason or reality. It has proved itself to have been a gigantic pipe-dream and, if we take heart manfully to face the true situation, however monstrous it may appear to us, it will in the end do us all the good in the world. The effort to disembarrass ourselves of a vast lumber of illusions calls for an elasticity of thought and a determination of character which have stood us in good stead throughout the many crises of our history.

How *can* we meet so unprecedented a crisis in such a way that the impossible becomes the practicable? The first answer, which actually embraces the whole answer, is to realize the quintessential importance of our own native countryside. Last in the estimation of intellectual and common man, politician and business-man alike, it has to come first. Suddenly, from having been a jaunting-ground, a recreation, a holiday, a means of extending our industrial works and housing schemes, a prey and a victim, it will have to fill the whole horizon of our thoughts and deeds as our life-line. The uses and abuses of our land-surface, hitherto a trifling affair except in the passing emergencies of war, have become the supreme issue of both the individual and the community, a literal matter of life or death.

*

Given a strictly limited area of land capable of growing crops and/or raising stock for the purpose of feeding our present population, it is evident that the abuse of land that might be productive to that end is a tragic impediment in solving the mathematical problem of fitting the amount of land needed to the quantity of population it is to maintain. Land thus put out of action—that is, used for other purposes than those of bearing food or simply abandoned to waste or exhausted in one way or another of its fertility, or underfarmed—is the sovereign issue. Do not let us run away with the comfortable notion that, even if much of this locked-up or unprofitable land were reclaimed for agriculture, we should be out of the wood. Far from it, even if we were to have the courage and resolution to restore it to its proper service. There still remains the need of increasing both the productivity and the fertility of land being already farmed. Mere tinkering with the issue will get us nowhere; better leave ill alone than act like Mr. Facing-Both-Ways in *The Pilgrim's Progress*.

Here, in broad outline and without going into a mass of confusing detail, are the figures of what agricultural land is already available to us and is farmed according to our present industrial and economic system, compared with those of land required to give the existing population of Great Britain and Northern Ireland an adequate diet. These figures are based upon the present estimated average yields of crops and livestock on the one hand, and upon the increased average annual yields of crops and livestock necessary for producing the same amount of food on the basis of optimum land-use, on the other. They are reliable figures, but our own view is that they err in being rather too cautious and conservative. All the same, they are acceptable so far as they go, for they are the fruit of a "Progress Report" drawn up by the Research Committee of the Rural Reconstruction Association, which is studying the extent to which the United Kingdom could become self-supporting in staple foodstuffs, and is derived from a prolonged study of Dr. Dudley Stamp's unique survey—*The Land of Britain: Its Use and Misuse*.[1]

The following are the acreage figures of the land now available: *Arable intensive*, 2,820,000; *Orchards and Fruit*, 845,000; *Arable Farm Crops*, 16,250,000; *Grassland*, 15,615,000; *Grand Total*, 35,530,000. Now for the land required: *Arable*, 28,886,000;

[1] Longmans, 1948.

Grassland, 19,467,000; *Fruit and Vegetables*, 1,200,000; *Grand Total*, 49,553,000. Next, the livestock (poultry, cattle, sheep, pigs and horses) available and required: 17,100,000 of the former; 29,810,000 of the latter. The principal increases needed are in cattle, roughly, 4 million; sheep, 5 million; pigs, 14 million and horses, 160,000. Rough grazings are excluded from these figures because, out of the 18 million acres of them we have, half are mountain-tops and the like, of very low productivity and the other half are counted as rough grazings both in actual and potential use. They are assigned by Dr. Stamp either to afforestation or for up-grading as grassland. Here, if we dare venture to say so, the Progress Report has not taken into consideration the immensity of the wastage in the "marginal" lands of Scotland and Wales.

Thus, in order to square the amount of land producing food with the numbers of the population consuming it, we are faced with a deficit of just under 40% or 14 million acres. Without question, this is the very lowest figure to be quoted and so barely on the right side of the line between enough and not enough to eat. For that very reason, we cannot rely simply on stepping up production of the farmland we still possess. It is, therefore, clear that the yields of those missing 14 million acres must come partly out of potentially agricultural land used for other purposes than those of food-production (that is, misused), and partly from intensifying existing but underfarmed arable, grassland and rough grazings. It must be both, not one or the other.

We shall then be changing over from an industrial to an agricultural primacy, growing new roots in our own land, changing over from a parasitic economics to real economy, beginning a new chapter in our history; and this most certainly cannot be done simply by grading up crop-production on what farms we already have. The Progress Report does not propose any change in our present very low standard of nutrition—that was hardly its business—but malnutrition is one of the worst headaches of our age. Even if we farmed every acre of the agricultural land which still survives, to the topmost pitch of intensity by one device after another—a goal we are nowhere near achieving—we should still need—and imperatively so—both to stop using up more agricultural land for industrial, housing and other non-agricultural purposes and to reconvert as many as possible of the acres already so abused or wasted to their original character. We simply cannot afford to go on treating farmland as a kind of Great Bed of Ware in which an expansive industrialism can stretch its monstrous limbs to their fullest capacity. But we have to go much further than that; we have to go backwards, to blot out and rewrite the manuscript of our immediate past.

We do not propose to plant a forest of figures into these pages in order to demonstrate to what extent our agricultural land has been diverted to uses or misuses fatal to any future prospect of keeping the wolf from the door. What we shall begin with are certain limited statistics to illustrate the extent, in particular directions, to which we have not only gambled away our natural wealth in the fundamentals of living—capital reserves that are the very reverse of a boundless fortune—but have also needlessly imperilled thereby our chances of escaping a destitution which is incomparably more serious than the loss of mere money.

Let there be no mistake: even in our most prosperous periods as an industrial nation, when the investments abroad were piling up, when vast areas of the entire globe were growing crops and raising sheep and cattle for our consumption, when the holds of countless ships were crammed with food for our shores, when the El Dorado of the world was more or less at our disposal as "the workshop of the world" and before many of the wheat-prairies of North America had turned to dust in growing our bread—even then the collapse of the whole system was a mere matter of time. It was as certain of failure as a policy must be which bound foreign peoples by economic law to wring food out of the soil at or below the cost of production, while completely ignoring the fact that other nations were just as capable as we were of building up manufactures that would make them independent of ours. Our industrial-economic system has operated for a hundred years with its eyes shut; had it so much as blinked them, it must have seen that to swallow up millions of our own good acres in order to make itself fatter and fatter was to put on full speed into the lean years to come. And even blinder than such blindness was it to depopulate the countryside of its countrymen in order to swell the corpulence of cities so bloated as to eat up miles of food-land at their doors. For the most fertile of surviving acres are misused when there are not enough skilled men to cultivate them.

*

First, take the most reasonable of all expansions into the country—housing; for, after all, people must be housed as well as fed. In sixty years (up to 1951), 5 million *arable* acres were lost to agriculture and of these, 655,836 were, according to Dr. Stamp, sacrificed during half that period (from 1901 to 1931) to urbanization alone. "Sacrificed" seems a hard term when it comes to having a roof over your head. But how actually unreasonable the housing spread has been, and is being, may be summed up in a sentence. By a kind of fatality, housing estates are almost invariably laid out on good agricultural land: A. G. Street's Ditchampton Farm being divided in half by a row of Council houses is one of countless examples.

But the most notorious example of perversity is the Thames Valley town of Slough. This valley contained some of the richest land in Britain, for the excellent reason that its low-lying alluvial soil was yet further fattened year by year by Thames mud. The Thames here is our English Nile, a river which has supported the ancient Egyptians for at least 6,000 years. In Victorian times, this treasury was recognized as such, for it supplied London with endless cartloads of vegetable produce, the carts returning with loads of horse-manure from the hansom-cabs of the city—a good example of the right kind of exchange between town and country. But when the modern Slough was first built, at a time when the hansom-cab had become obsolete, no space was found by the new houses for gardens—a good example of the worst kind of economy conceivable.

The point is important, and some protests have been made at this so far incorrigible habit of new towns seizing on land capable of intensive cultivation. This suicidal practice has been defended on the ground that the new town-gardens could produce more food than if this land were under the plough. How preposterous this defence is may be gathered from the fact that the most countrified of the new towns—Welwyn Garden City—has only 9% of its total area in food-producing gardens, while the average L.C.C. housing estate has only 5%. If, therefore, the policy of urban development on good land is to be continued in the future, at least one economy can be practised in the construction of new houses: they will save space, if not land, by leaving out the kitchens and larders.

Nor is there an indication at all of a change of policy in the siting of future new towns. In November, 1951, Dr. Stamp read a paper to the Royal Society of Arts in which he calculated that within the next twenty years the execution of our present housing programme, together with the extension of mineral workings and other industrial schemes in land under consideration, would demand anything from half a million acres as the lowest minimum, to 2½ million acres of what at present is open farmland, an area equivalent to the combined land-surface of Berkshire, Buckinghamshire, Oxfordshire, Hertfordshire and Bedfordshire. In July, 1952, Mr. R. T. Whitton, in his Presidential Address to the Chartered Auctioneers' and Estate Agents' Institute, remarked that urban development at the present rate was absorbing 80 square miles of farmland every year, and that was equivalent to a loss in foodstuffs of 2 million loaves of bread, 5,300 tons of cereals, 9,500 tons of potatoes, 600 tons of sugar, 150 tons of lamb and mutton, 350 tons of pig-meat, 75 tons of poultry, 8,750,000 eggs, 2 million gallons of milk and £100,000 worth of vegetables. Every ton of these had had to be replaced by purchases from abroad, often paid for out of hard currency. The position was made worse, Mr. Whitton continued, by the fact that a further 250,000 acres of "flat, well-drained agricultural land" were threatened by the new five-year plan. There is, therefore, no need to spend time or thought in the obvious conclusion that our civilization is engaged with the maximum of energy in putting itself to death.

Some of the most wanton and hair-raising examples of profligacy in British land policy, staking and losing the inheritance which by its own folly has become its only life-line, occur in the Northamptonshire iron industry and the extraction of ironstone, coal and gravel by opencast workings, again for the most part on fertile land. The frightful dereliction of areas so worked is an eyesore to every traveller, while the value as fuel of stone so extracted is very dubious. Part of the Lower Severn, for instance, rich in market-gardens and pasture, is scheduled for gravel-pits. Often the gravel and ironstone excavators fling out an overburden up to 80 feet thick, which, being impossible to replace, converts fruitful acres into slag-heaps. It is often said that all we have to do in opencast mining is to put back the topsoil. But nothing is said about such topsoil being cluttered up with hardcore, old bricks and other wastes, while the pits in the deeper workings can barely be restored at all. Iron ore and shaly coal are no doubt useful by-products of an industrial age. But even the machines cannot extract them unless the men who work them can be sure of a good meal.

Nor is the absorption of the higher classes of agricultural land by any means confined to the Fat Boy appetites of Suburbia, the New Towns and the extractive industries of minerals and metal. You have only to look out from the high ground over the rich Bedfordshire plain to see a forest of chimney-stacks sprawled over the landscape where they make Fletton bricks for the new towns which are to settle themselves over yet further slices of breakfast-, lunch- and dinner-land.

At least the brick-factories do make use of the clay at their feet. But a very large number of other factories of every type and operation, whose common likeness is that their functions have nothing whatever to do with the ground on which they are dumped, also share with one another the same unerring nose for the more productive acreages of farmland. Glance along the borderlands of the Great West Road, or indeed most of the great trunk lines for modern traffic radiating outwards from the cities, and note how the primary needs of bread and meat have been waved aside on behalf of secondary pleasures and industrial superfluities. As you drive along, the sight of these factories will tell you more than the most alarming statistics can do. They will tell you Part I of the story of the Prodigal Son in modern dress; they will show you him wasting his substance in riotous living. But if you do not see them with an eye that also sees beyond them, the *finale* of the fatted calf will be left out.

*

We turn now to another example of wasted land-surface because there is a good deal of confusion and uncertainty about it, even among those who are becoming aware, or have become so already, of the mortal danger of want in which we stand. We mean the activities of the Forestry Commission. Now, according to Sir George Stapledon,[1] the Commission had by that date (it was created by the Government in 1919) planted 131,000 acres with conifers and 7,000 acres with deciduous or hardwood trees. In 1943, a new scheme was set in motion of afforesting 3 million acres and replanting another 2 million acres. Unfortunately, Dr. Stamp[2] in giving these figures fails to state what proportion of hardwoods to conifers were planted between 1935 and 1948, the date of his book. But there can be no doubt at all that the numbers of hardwoods planted by the Commission in comparison with conifers is insignificant, a single drop in the full bucket.

[1] *The Land: Now and Tomorrow* (Faber, 1935). [2] *op cit.*, pp. 174-7.

This disproportion is of the first importance. Generally speaking, the Commission is an unpopular body. It is commonly felt that it uses its powers in a very arbitrary fashion, that it dispossesses too many sheep-farmers, that it fells too many of our existing woodlands to replace them with conifers, and that its conscript blocks of uniform firs or spruces are a blot on the landscape. On the other hand, it is more or less realized that this country is very short of timber, and, in fact, our forest-land has been reduced to 5% or 6% of the natural land-surface, so that we have become the worst forested countryside in Europe. And so the people who dislike the Commission's plantation policy but can present no definite, still less conclusive, case against it, shrug their shoulders and leave it at that.

We have ourselves seen a good deal of the mischief done by these Stygian and standardized conifers in North and South Wales, along the Marches and in the West of England. They offer inaccessible retreats for foxes, which emerge from them and prey on the lambs; they carve up the sheep-ranges of the hill-farmers; the trees are planted so close together that they provoke disastrous fires and infestations of parasites; they leave erosion scars when they are felled *en bloc* (as they must be and are); they are extremely ugly and ruin the diversity of our native landscapes. But these are only incidental reasons for the bad odour in which this policy is held, especially among local people who suffer from it.

We came to the conclusion that the really vital and unanswerable charge is that it is an *unecological* policy. The new term "ecology" is not at all an easy one to define. But, speaking broadly, it means the close adaptation in nature of particular plants and animals to the soil and physical environment of a particular region. It means the harmony, developed over aeons of time, between the living creature, its different fellows in the same habitat and the not-living habitat itself. In agriculture and forestry, it means the further adaptation of cultivated vegetation and domesticated animals to natural settings which vary in climatic and topographical conditions from place to place. That is to say, in man's relation to nature, ecology is the translation into fundamental human needs of what amounts in the wild state to a natural law. If, for instance, you try to grow wheat on a mountainside with a heavy rainfall, you are being taught by your failure the elements of ecology.

But ecology is more than this. The object of the ecologist is a dual one. His first aim is to discover and define the highly complex associations between soil, plant, animal and landscape; his next, to re-establish man as the responsible and perceiving manager or steward of this earthly and interrelated estate. Our own Elizabethans, Shakespeare among them, were firmly convinced that a "chain of being" between man, nature and the supernatural existed throughout the universe. This is a very useful term to apply, however it be interpreted, to the greatest issue of our time, the cultivation of the soil to feed the people. It is indeed the only valid antitoxin to the fashionable modern theory of "the conquest of nature". In fact, ecology is the modern equivalent of the old-fashioned idea of good husbandry, with the difference that it embraces a wider circle of knowledge than that of traditional experience in running a farm. The farm of the ecologist is the whole earth and the farmer the human race in its due relation to it.

How, then, does the Forestry Commission violate ecology? By planting conifers of the same or closely related species in solid masses, more often than not on hillsides? The answer is best given in *Mountains and Moorlands*,[1] by Dr. W. H. Pearsall, F.R.S., the Quain Professor of Botany at London University. The firs or spruces are planted in dense cubes because they yield a packed crop in the shortest possible time. The object of so doing is a commercial and industrial one, not one of good husbandry, and so of true ecology. For the same reason, the plantation is clear-felled at maturity and forms a "close canopy" which has "the great biological disadvantage" of killing out all growth on the forest floor and so precluding

[1] Collins, 1950.

"any natural regeneration". Both the gloomy shade and the carpet of needles replace a natural humus with "an acid surface layer". This forms what is called *mor*, a highly acid soil which lacks earthworms, nitrates and bacteria. The final stage is reached after the clear-felling. For this exposed, acid and beggared soil is at once at the mercy, especially on slopes, of the rains and the winds, which sweep away the impoverished soil as dust or mud, leaving only an eroded surface good for nothing but a harsh and scanty growth of the toughest kind of weeds.

It is thus a matter of urgency to deal at some length with the conifer policy of the Commission, whose ambition it is to cover no fewer than 800,000 acres of Wales alone with such plantations. The effect is bound to be precisely the opposite of mixed hardwood forest on hill or mountain slopes. These are genuinely ecological, not only controlling and balancing but actually insuring the water-supply, enriching the soil with humus from the decaying leaves, mitigating any severity of climate, sheltering and protecting both the slopes and the fields below. But the monocultural conifer block in the end destroys the soil altogether, whether for sheep or woodland or arable crops, and so actually does more harm than the factory or the new town, which locks up the soil for food-bearing purposes, but does not destroy it. The conifer policy, is, in fact, a perfect example of the direct clash between the industrial and the ecological points of view, between an urban and an agricultural civilization.

One of the most pregnant sayings of the great Dutch ecologist, Dr. Ehrenfeld Pfeiffer, is that, if the hills degenerate, so does the culture of a nation. It is impossible to stop the rot in the hill-lands of Britain, especially in Scotland and Wales, and so to increase the meat-supplies they are able to furnish, unless, in Pfeiffer's words, "a biological study of landscapes" replaces the fallacious test of economics. This degeneration is not, of course, the consequence only of the mass-production of conifers for pit-props and other industrial purposes. In Scotland, for instance, 4 million acres have fallen out of agricultural use. The spread of deer-forest—which, properly speaking, is not forest at all but a wilderness of scrub, heath, gorse and bracken—is mainly responsible for this dereliction. Between 1883 and 1938, the deer-forest had usurped no fewer than 3½ million acres of Scottish marginal land, the crofter population had shrunk to a fraction of what it once was and, since the Highland enclosures or "Clearances" in the last century, the sheep had driven out the beef-cattle. In 1794, for instance, there was a total of 2,140 head of cattle (winter stock) in the Small Isles of Eigg, Canna, Rum and Muck, while the human population was 1,339, engaged in kelp-gathering, fishing and farming. Today, there are under 500 head of cattle wintering in these Isles and the farmers and fishermen are down to less than 200.

Our economic system has been based on the absurdity that frozen meat from the Argentine and elsewhere is regarded as a "superior economy" to procuring it fresh from the Welsh and Scottish hills, now largely derelict as a result, while the weekly meat-ration is inadequate; a biting enough comment on the Cloud-cuckoo-land of that system. But the futility is even more crass, for, instead of reclaiming and restocking these desolate mountain-lands of the North and West, we have preferred to squander millions of pounds in East and West Africa, Queensland and British Honduras in hair-brained schemes more fantastic than the South Sea Bubble, for extracting vast quantities of poultry, oils and fats at short notice, which have left desert conditions behind them. We have not even kept up the figures of our sheep, either arable sheep on the downs and lowlands or long-wooled grazing sheep on the highlands. Between 1874 and 1938 we had lost not only 6 million acres of arable land but 5 million sheep, while the folded flock, invaluable for maintaining the fertility of chalk and other lighter lands for corn-crops to follow "the golden hoof", has been virtually banished to the ghostly hinterland of old-fashioned or "backward" husbandry.

Oh but, the efficiency expert replies, since 1938 we have

changed all that and made agriculture a stable industry. Have we indeed? We should like to take him a tour of the marginal lands in Wales and the Border which we know fairly well (the same applies to Scotland) and show him mile after mile after mile of what was once good pasture reverted to mat-grass or blue-grass, but principally to bracken. Sixteen years ago, Sir George Stapledon gave the figure for bracken-infested pasture in Wales at 152,000 acres. It is certainly much greater now. In the days of "backward" husbandry, the bracken was kept at bay by human labour, ponies and wethers (wethers or wedders being ram or tup lambs after castration; but wethers became "uneconomic"), and these were of crucial value not only as bracken-eaters but as leaders and four-footed shepherds of the hill-flocks—when the family demand changed from large to small joints. The ponies, the human shepherds and the sheep-farmers disappeared, the roofs of the farmsteads fell in owing to "uneconomic" prices and the bracken took possession of a stage left empty by the gradual exodus of both human and animal inhabitants. Depopulation both in hill-stock and sheep-farmers has been the richest possible fertilizer for—bracken. Stapledon has rammed this lesson home in detail. In the meantime, not only are those 14 million additional acres unavailable which are needed to make us self-supporting and so to escape from famine, but this area grows daily larger.

*

Pass on now from the marginal lands which are so remote from an urban civilization that they suffer more from neglect and decay than from exploitation,[1] to what is part of its very core—the transport system. The census of roads in Great Britain made by Dr. Stamp for the years 1937-8, and allowing for an average width of seven yards, reached the extraordinary figure of 457,240 acres, as compared with 250,000 acres for the railways. Later developments in road-making must have

[1] But we have examples of the latter to give later.

carried this figure beyond the half-million mark. Nor do these figures take into consideration the enormous waste in the grass verges of our roads, enough to give a square meal to a million tethered cows, sheep and goats every day. For they represent an area of at least 5,000 farms of average size. But unthrift in these grass-borders is taken for granted and all the roadmen do is to cut the grass when it grows too rank and high, not for the sake of the fodder or bedding or compost-making, since they leave it where it lies or, worse still, burn it, but simply for the sake of the roads.

Nothing could bring home more vividly to the reader the extreme incompatibility between an industrial and an agricultural civilization. In spite of the luxury of our road system, it is actually deficient in access to farms, especially in outlying regions. In the country, only a pair of hedges, and sometimes not even these, separate the arterial roads from the adjacent farmlands, and yet these neighbours are not on speaking terms. It is not only that our main roads as often as not cut off the farms from their bartons and outbuildings and slice up the farm-fields. You have only to compare them in this respect with the unimproved English lanes and byways, many of which survive in the courses and directions laid out for them by our Saxon forefathers, who *were* an agricultural people, and therefore unbedevilled by the modern craze for getting from one place to another in the shortest possible time. These were always integrated with the farm economy.

But our arterial roads are mainly a vast network of communication between the big towns, docks, harbours, factories and the metropolis; industrial works, not to mention ribbon development, stud their borders and the farmlands that grow food for the people to eat are so much space between one "conurbation" or pleasure resort and another. You have but to stand on the edge of a meadow or cornfield and look over the edge at the traffic passing along the high-road, to realize that the few steps between them are as wide as a continent. The weed-seeds float unlawfully from field to field, but it is rare to see any cracks or holes in the road. The road is rarely empty and silent; the field except at long intervals rarely otherwise.

It is a pity that no statistics exist to compare the numbers of workmen employed on the roads with those of the farmers and farm-labourers in the fields. Indeed, our transport system is very similar to that of the Roman Empire, in which all roads led to Rome. The Empire crashed for that very reason. Once the Italian peasantry had been dispossessed and had drifted into Rome to receive their bread and circuses, the provinces had only to stop the road-traffic for the Rome of the Caesars to perish. Our main roads are, in fact, city-bred; so far as the country which produces food is concerned, they are nothing but stripes flogged across its shoulders.

A word as to hedges. It is not in many places that we can look over them from our meadow or cornfield, because the art of laying or "pleaching" or "plushing" them in diagonal lines with a "heathering" of whippy bramble rods has fallen on evil days, like so many other serviceable country crafts. Your mechanical hedge-cutter can make nothing like so seemly and useful a job. In some areas, too, notably in East Anglia, hedges have been grubbed up altogether to condition the land to the machine. This is a kind of bastard prairie-farming in imitation of American methods and highly conducive to the effect it has had on the Great Plains—namely, land-erosion or "blowing". And this conversion of soil into dust does occur, and has occurred, in our own country, particularly in Fenland, through overcropping and lack of shelter-belts, whether of tree or hedgerow. Hedges and hedge-timber play an extremely important part in our island ecology, not only as wind-breaks, as nurseries for insectivorous birds and for other beneficial purposes; they are an indispensable part of the pattern of our native agriculture, and their removal is one more example of the abuse of land to serve an industrial end in contrast and conflict with a conserving, fostering and truly economic one.

We are equally lavish with our very limited acreage of available land in two opposite extremes that preoccupy the modern world—building up huge military establishments, and offsetting the dreariness of modern factory work and the stress and strain of modern life by sport and recreation. In respect of the former, Dr. Stamp puts the pre-war acreage of "land agriculturally unproductive, including airfields, training grounds, etc." at 1,399,000. This, he says, has increased in our decade to 2,250,000, adding the pious hope that the bulk of land taken for airfields, military camps and the like will be from "what was formerly heathland and moorland". To anybody who, for instance, has noticed the dereliction of the farms in Dorset's Isle of Purbeck, which is nearly all in military hands, this is a sanguine expectation indeed.

As for school and college playing fields, parks and sports and recreation grounds, the acreage figure for golf-links alone in 1936 was 130,000, and heaven knows what it is for dog-racing tracks, racing stables and other hardly less generous appropriations of food-potential land for pleasure and sport. Nobody in his senses would clamour for the ploughing-up of our cricket-fields, and it is, of course, true that the sites of not a few golf-courses are sand-dunes. But what would you have: enough land to feed the people of Britain—and that means somehow and somewhere finding another 14 million acres—or playing eighteen holes on an empty stomach? It is more than time to bring home the brutal fact that each Briton in our Islands has just 0·8 of an acre of his homeland from which to still the cravings of his belly. He and she must take their choice, either to frame a new policy which will squarely meet such a reality or to take the way of want. For the foreigner will be growing his percentage of land for his own need. And, talking of parks, let us be done with the prejudiced nonsense that is often tossed up against the parklands of the 18th century. We forget that in Queen Anne's reign one-quarter of the population were farmers, and that these parklands were laid out with a view to a balance between timber and grazing land by a landed gentry highly skilled in the arts of husbandry. Can the same or anything like it be said of our parks? It was *after* the Industrial Revolution, when the Georgian landed estate was ornamentally promoted to be the Victorian "gentleman's seat", that the use of land became ostentatious and so profligate.

All the diversities in this wastage of land must be paralleled by the equally varied wastage of water, for both in agriculture and ecology land and water are inseparable. It is hardly credible that, no provision for storage being made for it, we waste practically all the rainfall the bounty of our climate grants us. It is none of our doing that it refreshes the fields, replenishes the springs and maintains the water-table. Against drought we have no advantage from the clouds that preceded it. On the other hand, our consumption of the water with which nature has endowed us without stint is of an extravagance so prodigious that we have succeeded in considerably lowering a water-table that in the pre-industrial era must have been one of the highest in Europe. Under modern conditions we expend 30 gallons of water per cow per day, while in the up-to-date cowhouses rarely is any attempt made to pipe and utilize the invaluable resources of urine supplied gratis by the cows. Modern dairying, in fact, consumes 3,000 gallons a day per 100 head of cattle, while the overhead irrigation of the modern market-gardens, not to mention the prodigal use of water in the silk and paper industries, is even more spendthrifty. "The modern *per capita* consumption in a town", to quote Dr. Stamp,[1] "is between 20 and 30 gallons compared with perhaps the use of 2 gallons per head under primitive conditions."

An industrial civilization has thrust upon us the paradox of allowing our rainfall to run to waste, while proper land-use in the country is badly impeded by the lack of adequate water-supply on numbers of the more rural farms. What is even more notorious is the squandering both of natural resources and of farmland in the upland catchment areas by such reservoirs as that of the Elan Valley and Lake Vyrnwy in Wales, Thirlmere and Haweswater in the Lakes and on the Pennine Watershed.

[1] *op. cit.*, p. 242.

Recently, it has been proposed to flood the whole of the five-mile-long Honddu Valley in the Black Mountains, which has been an agricultural region of sheepwalks, cattle-raising, shelter-belts of mixed woodland and small arable fields ever since the foundation of Llanthony Priory there in the 12th century. The whole point of these grandiose schemes is that they are plotted for industrial and urban usage at the expense of the local and regional population. Even more profligate are the hydro-electric schemes, not for supplying electricity to the regions where they are hatched but for speeding up the export trade. The Electricity Board, for instance, proposes to acquire 30,000 acres of good marginal land by Plynlimon for a hydro-electric plan whereby the headwaters of the Wye, the Severn, the Rheidol, the Lerry and lesser streams are to be diverted into artificial channels by tunnels to make a series of huge reservoirs, shrinking the great rivers of the West into mere drains. And how much land, we wonder, has been "sterilized" by the water-companies?

Yet the actual water-traffic of our rivers and canals is rapidly coming to an end. In spite of its numerous weirs, the Lower Wye was once one of the busiest of waterways for merchandise, though it is rare nowadays to see so much as a rowing-boat on it. The merest glance at Constable's oil paintings of his native Stour in Suffolk shows how busy with barges the little river was in the early 19th century. Constable's father was a miller, and from his mill at Nayland 1,400 sacks of flour were loaded into barges in a week. Constable's paintings educate the eye to perceiving the barges and the watermills as the organic link between the river and the cornfields on its banks. Now the river-bed is choked with rush and waterweed, the current is slowed up, the Dedham willows he painted have been killed by the ingress of salt water, the mills are picturesque ruins and never a boat is to be seen. Thus, an industrial civilization starves the land on the one hand, and squanders it on the other.

It may well be asked—what *does* it use its rivers for? One way is to poison them with industrial effluents so that edible fish are destroyed in millions. Nor is such pollution confined to the rivers, as witness that of coastal waters and oil discharge into the sea, murdering fish, birds and micro-organisms. Another way is to hurry the water off as fast as may be to the sea as though it had only a nuisance-value, straitening the reaches and cutting down the bank-protecting willows and alders to that end. When a heavy rainfall occurs, there is extreme flooding, but the deliberate flooding of the water-meadows by the "drowner" for the sake of an "early bite" for stock is regarded as old-fashioned husbandry. And what could be more futile than to build dams and dykes against floods, but neglect clothing the denuded watersheds with the proper vegetation to prevent flooding by the run-off of the waters and the silt blocking up the mouths of the rivers?

In the 18th century the Thames Estuary was rich with gardens and orchards. Standing on Shooter's Hill above Woolwich, Celia Fiennes, the diarist, described the prospect in 1697 as,

> a vast tract of land, which appears in the greatest variety, some lands cloathed with trees, others with grass and flowers, gardens, orchards, with all sorts of herbage and tillage, with several little towns all by the river.

This is an ecological picture; yet now, when we desperately need every yard of good land to keep us alive, the former fertile lands between Gravesend and Woolwich "have become London's backyard . . . vast refuse dumps, smouldering, noisome and rat-infested",[1] while the outfall sewers of the London drainage system pour out millions of tons, taking with them enough fertility in minerals and other wastes to feed whole counties. As a people, we have the qualities to survive; as the industrial civilization of today, we neither can nor deserve to do so.

Just as water is the corollary to land, so skilled labour is the

[1] *The Thames from Source to Mouth*, by L. T. C. Rolt (Batsford, 1951).

corollary to land-use. Men are in fact the best crop the land produces, and so the loss of men from the land is the worst example of its misuse. The ebbing tide of labour from the land has persisted for rather more than a hundred years, roughly speaking from the General Enclosure Act of 1845 to the present day. Enclosure, of course, had been in operation for many years before 1845, and what enclosure did was to turn peasants into paupers and landless labourers. It is, however, a mistake to make enclosure as such the villain of the piece. Our countryside recovered from the Tudor Enclosures, while enclosure by mutual agreement was a common practice in the latter part of the Middle Ages. The whole point of the eighteenth- and nineteenth-century enclosures was that they were effected by a class-war between the greater and the lesser landed interests, between the landlord and the peasant, a war in which one class became the helpless victim of the other and the peasantry was transformed into a wage-proletariat. And just when this revolutionary event occurred, another was "mewing its mighty youth", that of the Industrial Revolution, which took final advantage of the breach the enclosures had forced.

For a time an uneasy equilibrium, especially during the Napoleonic Wars, was maintained between "high farming" and the new factory-towns that it fed. But high farming was only an interval of suspension and, whether by taxation, the soaring of the national expenditure, the break-up of the village craftsmen who were interdependent with the farmers and land-workers, by cheap mass production, the stringency of the Game Laws and the absorption of the new rural proletariat into the slums and the "dark Satanic mills", the old balance between town and country was dislocated and Waterloo proved to be the costliest victory in our history. The next fatality was the repeal of the Corn Laws in the cause of cheap imported food for the new industrial masses, and 300,000 labourers left the land in thirty years. Between 1871 and 1931, the farm-workers dropped from 676,000 to 383,000, the farmers themselves from 24 per square mile to 20, and the rural population as a whole from 180–200 per square mile to 100–120; while between 1874 and 1945 land-workers per 100 acres declined from 4·7% to 2·9%. Thus, by this and other erosive processes we became what Christopher Turnor[1] called "the least land-minded of all peoples". The psychological effects of this depopulation have been even more disastrous, for they have helped to make us a bone-lazy and pleasure-loving people by reaction against the awful monotony and irresponsibility of factory work. For nobody can call sitting at a conveyor belt real work.

It is a matter neither of bias nor of propaganda, neither of bees in the bonnet nor of bats in the belfry, neither of "idealism" nor of a romantic infatuation with the past, but the plainest of plain facts that, as our industrial civilization sowed the wind in dishonour, so now it is on the eve of reaping the whirlwind. And the fundamental cause of this bad beginning and worse ending ahead is not the abuses of the system, the worst of which like poverty and the Poor Law have been patched up, not primarily the reasons put forward by reformers of one kind and another, but one simple and all-embracing historical event. It is the loss of the balance between town and country; that is to say, the sacrifice of foundations to an industrial superstructure. Our society has become an inverted pyramid as a consequence of the long chain of events which took their rise from the dispossession of the peasantry. Congested cities and an emptied countryside are the deep-seated disease which is devouring us. Therefore, the loss of what industrialists call "man-power" from the land is the climax of that crowded picture of derelict, wasted and misused land which has been the subject of this chapter.

It is vital to the issue before us that we should not fail to note that this seepage of land-workers from the land is still going on. There is no indication at all that it has stopped or is drawing to an end. Yet in another sense it must soon come to an end, for now the reservoir of labour for the land has shrunk to

[1] *Yeoman Calling* (Chambers, 1939).

between 5% and 6% of the entire population. If any reader believes it to be within the bounds of possibility for this minute percentage to provide our teeming numbers with "an adequate diet", he is Humpty-Dumpty just before he fell off the wall. You might as well expect a leaf-cutting ant to keep an elephant well fed. And without meaning to make the reader's flesh creep, we should state that the quality of this loss is even more serious than the quantity, for it is the skilled all-rounder who has been the chief element in that loss.

Yet we are faced with the uncompromising fact that the industrial mind refuses to contemplate a fully-manned countryside. Every shade of orthodox political opinion is unanimous about this, whether Left, like Bateson and Orwin, or Right, like Astor and Rowntree. The economists speak with the same voice, as any reader of *The Economist* during the past twenty years can verify for himself. In *The English Village*,[1] by Victor Bonham-Carter, it is expressly declared, not argued, that to meet the present emergency small farms must be only slightly increased and "the number of agriculturists" not at all. It is not relevant here to summarize the arguments and theories advanced by this dominant school of thought to justify the *status quo* and reject the only remedy for it—the re-population of the land. They are a purely abstract and industrial pleading and they are based upon a hypothesis that is no longer tenable —namely, that food will continue to be "cheap" and that, despite the fact that world-populations are already outrunning their food-supplies, despite a falling land-fertility rate almost everywhere and despite the fact that our own bargaining powers are stultified by adverse trade balances, foreign nations will continue to pour food imports into our harbours.

Furthermore, these abstractions cling to the fallacy that "output per man" (which means fewer and fewer men producing more and more crops) is a superior standard of measurement to that of output per acre, and that power-machinery more than compensates for starving the land of men. We know

[1] Pelican Books, 1952.

of a farm whose labour-staff once numbered forty before it became fully mechanized. Now the forty are reduced to four. The astounding thing is that a pauperism like this is hailed by the agronomists and economists as a triumph of modern progress over the uneconomic past. The situation on which this theoretic economics was based is, like "the cloud-capped towers, the gorgeous palaces" of Prospero's vision, already "melted into air, into thin air". The point is that the drainage of men from the land is inseparable from its neglect and abuse.

One last conclusion. The terrible hardships and poverty suffered by the peasants after the enclosures had driven them off their holdings, together with the skinflint wages paid them as landless labourers all through the 19th century, might easily have misled a historian who failed to compare past with present to assume that the wage-system was responsible for rural depopulation. Why, then, do the landsmen continue to desert the land when their hours have been lessened and their wages increased to compare not unfavourably with those of the towns?

Assuredly, the answer lies elsewhere. But this must form the subject of future chapters. The proposition as it stands is that lack of enough land and lack of enough men to husband it, abused land and underfarmed land are insuperable obstacles to building a self-supporting nation. A generous increase in the acreage of the land, the numbers of the men, the productiveness of the farms and the fertility of the soil are indispensable means for removing those obstacles. The old world of the economists is at the point of death and a new world in the pangs of birth.

CHAPTER IV

What We Eat and Where It Could Come From

We have now dealt, however roughly and tersely, with the subject of our food and its sources, and we have followed this up with a study of the abuse of our land, in which so much more of our food could be grown. In Chapter V we deal, in broad terms, with the proper use of land. Here we are concerned to refer back to Chapter II, and to suggest a few—a very few—of the possible ways of making up for foreign food sources, as and when we lose them.

BREAD

It is probable that we shall not be able to supply ourselves with all the bread we need off our own soil until our population is much reduced, unless we have a major social and psychological revolution. As we saw in Chapter II, we produce at home only 29% of the wheat consumed. In 1951, over 2 million acres of our arable land (2,131,000) was devoted to wheat, out of an arable total of nearly 18 million acres (17,998,000). The wheat acreage was thus over 10% of the total. This may not seem, to the townsman, a large percentage to be devoted to bread, but we are not free to increase it as we might wish. Quite apart from the fact that wheat acreage can only be increased at the expense of other crops almost as important, wheat will not grow in all the soils and climates of these islands. This is immediately apparent if we glance at the figures for Scotland, 70,000 acres, or Northern Ireland, only 1,000 acres, whereas England and Wales grow 2,060,000 acres. England and Wales grow 300,000 acres *more* wheat than oats; Scotland grows more than twelve times as much oats as wheat; Northern Ireland more than three hundred times as much oats as wheat.

Very large acreages at present devoted to grass, to fodder crops and to vegetables and orchards could, technically, grow wheat. Supposing, for a moment, that the problem were *merely* one of soil and climate, it would be possible to find about 9,400,000 acres in the United Kingdom where wheat could be grown with a reasonable chance of success. This would mean that we need import no wheat at all. But it would also mean reducing our home production of milk and meat to an insignificant fraction of the present figure. It would mean, what is more, abusing our soil. The fact is that although, facing a total failure of imports, our obvious salvation would be to become a bread-eating people, we could not do it for long. The quality of soil required to grow wheat is best maintained by animal manure, applied in the simplest way by planting that soil to lucerne and other temporary grasses at certain intervals, and putting cattle to graze on them. And this leads to an interesting conclusion: in theory, with a "given" number of acres, we can eat *either* bread *or* meat and milk. And, in fact, if we look no further than ten years ahead, this is true. A dictator with total power today could, by giving an order and enforcing it, enable us to reap a wheat harvest in excess of 5 million tons next year. Or, if, like Lord Woolton, he had a fixation on red meat, he could, by denying us bread, feed us on home-fed beef. But the policy could only be a short-term one, because where, as in Britain, limitation of space entails, as an essential of survival, maintenance of soil fertility, the only safe farming for the highest possible productiveness is high mixed farming.

Are we, then, unable to increase the wheat acreage? We do not believe this to be so. The acreage under wheat could certainly be doubled on several conditions. One, that permanent pastures, however good, be ploughed and treated as arable, becoming temporary pasture at intervals; two, that far more arable land be periodically rested and enriched by becoming temporary pasture planted to deep-rooted grasses and "weeds"; three, that as fast as permanent pasture in suitable climates and on suitable soils is ploughed for arable, steps be taken to reclaim, for fine pasture, some of the 17 million acres of rough grazing available.

Whichever way we turn in search of room to plant wheat, we are forced in the end to return to the waste entailed in our own 17 million acres of "rough grazing". It is a luxury we can no longer afford. Granted that a great deal of it is too difficult to claim—mountainsides and tops, for example, or moorland, good only for sheep. The fact remains that perhaps as much as 8 million acres could be turned first into improved pasture, subsequently into arable land. This reclamation alone would make us self-supporting in wheat and meat. To the claim that this reclamation is a technical impossibility, we reply by pointing to what Lord Iveagh has done at Elveden[1] with heath land, or, going further back into agricultural history, to what Coke did in Norfolk, turning a miserable sandy waste, where it was said one could see "one blade of grass with two rabbits fighting for it", into rich, productive land in a couple of decades.

The difficulties in the way of our becoming self-supporting in the matter of bread are *not* technical, nor even difficulties of space. They are psychological and social difficulties. The whole past of the English people until only a century ago or a little more, is one of a small population living on a fertile soil with apparently infinite room for expansion. We do not think of agricultural land as valuable at all; in fact, the price of land, if it is called agricultural land, is about one-tenth of the price when it is called building land. That fact alone is immensely significant. Peoples who, in the past, have faced a situation in which, from their cultural beginnings, land for crops has been in short supply have been able, nevertheless, to expand and become great by treating the land they had as precious, and by *making soil*. Surely we, with our enormous technical advantages and our powerful machines, can be as ingenious as the ancient Peruvians who, with no iron tools and not even draught animals, let alone machines, created millions of acres of arable soil in terraces on the western face of the Andes?

[1] See *The Elveden Enterprise* by George Martelli (Faber, 1952).

The problem of bread, then, can be summed up as follows. We *can* double our wheat harvest, and perhaps grow all our own bread, provided we push the plough into some of our 13,000 acres of permanent grass; that we can only do this at the expense of milk and meat *unless* we maintain and even increase our head of stock by turning rough grazings into fine pasture and subsequently into arable and temporary pasture; that to a nation in straits for food, an acre is more productive under wheat than under grass for cattle; that—and we shall go into this later—bread is worth whatever it costs to grow and ought not to be regarded as something which must "pay" or be cheap compared with bread from imported wheat. It must be made worth the farmer's while to grow all the wheat he can; for it is worth the nation's while, at any price.

OATS AND BARLEY

Of these two grains, much less need be said. We already grow 97% of our oats, and could grow 100% without difficulty. So we can dismiss oats at once, with only this note: we can always use more of it if we are to maintain and increase our head of stock while decreasing feeding-stuffs imports.

Of barley, we already grow about 70% at home, which requires about 1,900,000 acres of land—173,000 acres in Scotland, the rest, but for 3,000 acres in Northern Ireland, grown in England and Wales. To become entirely self-supporting, we should have to find a further 600,000 acres. The problem is largely one of space only, in this case, barley being hardier than wheat. It would unquestionably be possible to find these acres—on exactly the same conditions as we discussed in the case of wheat. It is simply a matter of disregarding the financial cost of land reclamation and land-use changes.

We are well aware of the arguments in favour of maintaining, as pasture, certain particularly fine permanent pastures, and of those against reclamation of heath-land, rough grazing, mountain land, and so forth. The first were sound enough when we could afford to eat beef and buy bread, pork and mutton overseas. This is no longer our case. However fine the beef, or milk, deriving from a certain permanent pasture, if that piece of land will grow grain one year in three, and feed cows or beef in one year in three, by treating it as a ley, then so it should be treated: the food value, in bread and pork, of an acre of grain is much greater than its food value in beef, under grass. *Until we reclaim some of our 17 million acres* of "rough grazing"—a euphemism for neglected land—we cannot afford to eat beef.

OILS AND FATS

The subject of oils and fats, including butter, can only be dealt with in association with that of milk. We have, in Britain, only two sources of edible fat (other than sea fish). These are pigs and cows; and lard and butter were virtually the only fats, other than fat consumed with meat, which were eaten in Britain until the invention of margarine. Margarine and "cooking fat" are made from tropical vegetable oils and from whale oil. The supply of whale oil is limited and cannot be increased significantly. Tropical oils are, in the context of this book, undesirable by definition as imported food, though, we repeat, this does not mean that we are "against" importing them on principle. Let us import, by all means, as much as we can honestly pay for with manufactures genuinely required by the oil-producer. Meanwhile, can we increase our own domestic fat supply?

The home production of lard can obviously be increased by increasing the home production of pigs. This is in fact being done, but the problem is not an easy one. Pigs are not, primarily, grass-eating animals, but compete directly with human beings for their dinner. They thrive on the same foods which we eat—grain, vegetables and even meat. Consequently, the pig cannot be regarded, like the sheep or the cow or a wheat plant, as a device for turning soil, which human beings cannot consume directly, into human food. The pig is simply a machine which processes one kind of potentially human food into another. For instance, pigs are fed on barley: but human beings can eat barley; or you can feed pigs on potatoes—which we might just as well eat ourselves.

However, the pig is not a mere luxury. Its manure alone is of very great use. Quality and nature of food are important, as well as quantity, and pork, bacon and lard are agreeable and nourishing foods, not to speak of ham, brawn, chitterlings, sausages and the rest. Moreover, pigs will consume food which, although it contains nourishment that human beings could use directly, is too coarse and nasty for us. For example, swill made from our own food wastes. In the past, pigs were particularly valuable because, herded in the oak forests, they ate acorns and wild roots which contain nourishment capable of supporting men, but are so unpalatable that they have been regarded as food only in times of famine. Pigs relish snails—a very rich food which most English people do not care for.

In short, there are two ways of feeding pigs: to get the very finest, highly standardized carcases, they must be fed on barley, maize, potatoes, and—of this more to follow—butter-milk. But perfectly good pigs—a source of all good pig-meats and of lard—can be produced on swill made from food wastes, on small potatoes, windfall fruits, snails, acorns and so forth, with some barley or maize-meal for fattening. This second kind of pigs are cottagers' pigs, smallholders' pigs, the pigs of our pig clubs. The work of increasing the pig population in this class has been undertaken, and is being admirably pressed, by the Village Produce Association, and that admirable body, and others doing similar work, ought to be encouraged by every possible means.

Even so, we shall need an increased barley crop. We could, of course, feed more pigs if we made less beer—this is only too often pointed out by bodies advocating abstinence from alcoholic liquors. We, in our turn, must point out that we could buy enough grain to feed millions of pigs with the money we spend on tea, not to mention coffee and tobacco. Let us leave beer alone—although it is a pity we no longer brew it ourselves and so have a drink with some body and quality to it. In any case, we have already discussed the question of increasing our barley acreage.

For the rest, the increase of our home lard supply, by increasing the pig population, is intimately associated with the increase of our butter supply. The vast Danish pig industry might almost be considered as a by-product of the Danish dairy-farming industry; for the kind of pigs which we mentioned first—the super-carcases, not the cottage pigs—are best fed on barley and butter-milk.

Butter-milk is the fluid remaining after cream has been turned into butter. We will deal with this aspect of lard-production when we come, shortly, to butter.

MILK, BUTTER AND CHEESE

As we saw in Chapter II, we import 93% of our butter, and 74% of our cheese. If we are to increase our total home production of fats, we must not only make good these imports, but produce even more than that, or we shall only have secured our present ration without increasing it. This is probably "impossible", but we have no alternative, and must at least try.

The cattle and sheep of Britain, whether for milk or meat are fed off:

84,000 acres of lucerne (a fodder).

About 3 million acres of clover, sainfoin and other fodder-crops grown on arable land and mowed for one kind or another of winter "keep" (hay, silage, dried grass).

About 2¾ million acres of the same, but grown for grazing, not mowing.

About 3 million acres of permanent grass mown for "keep".

About 10 million acres of permanent grass for grazing.

17 million acres of "rough grazing".

Imported and domestic "concentrates", i.e. oil-cakes, etc. (See Chapter II).

An immense quantity of this food is turned into milk by cows. In the year July, 1951—June, 1952 British cows produced *1,536 million gallons of milk*!

Now, of this sea of milk, no less than 1,369 million gallons was consumed in liquid form. There are about 50 million people, men, women and children, in the United Kingdom; so apparently if we all drank it, average consumption was 27 gallons 1 quart 1 pint of milk in the year, or little less than 4½ pints a week.

Is this a good way of consuming milk-food? Probably it is not. Milk is, of course, a perfect food for infants, but the digestion of an infant differs from that of an adult, and raw milk for all above the infant age is not particularly easy to digest. However, milk is a valuable food, but almost certainly more valuable if it is processed into three other kinds of food—butter, cheese and pork—or bacon.

Of our total milk production, 167 million gallons are already made into butter, cheese and dried or condensed milk; also, we regret to report, into industrial goods of several kinds.

Let us suppose that we cut our average consumption of milk to 2¼ pints a week—the infants still receiving all they need, since our figure is an average-per-head. This would be no hardship to adults, nor to children above "infant" status, since most children dislike milk and much of that forced on the poor creatures is wasted. In that case, we should have available 689½ million gallons for processing. For the sake of this argument (the sole object of which is to have this question thoroughly discussed and not to lay down the law), we will suppose half of this milk supply allocated to butter-making, half to cheese.

To make one pound of butter, 2·358 gallons of milk are required. We could, therefore, make 146 million pounds, that is about 65,000 tons, of butter per annum. Our actual production is 25,000 tons, our imports are 335,000 tons. The figures would, if the ration were left as it stands, become 90,000 tons and 270,000 tons respectively—a healthier picture. But no gain, excepting in imports saved.

There would, however, be a gain worth considering: some hundreds of thousands of gallons of butter-milk capable of fattening a vast number of pigs—and therefore of turning our milk not only into butter, but also into lard, not to mention pork, bacon and the rest.

Meanwhile, we are still left with about 341 million gallons of liquid milk to turn into about 345 million pounds of cheese.[1] That is about 154,000 tons per annum. *Our total imports of cheese are exactly* (*1950*) *154,000 tons*. So that we could, by reducing our milk consumption to half the present figure, but maintaining the same head of milk cattle:

(*a*) Increase our home butter supply from 7% to 25% of total present consumption.

(*b*) Increase our home cheese supply from 26% to 100% of the total present consumption.

(*c*) Increase our home production of lard, pork, bacon, etc., by a very large amount which we have been unable to estimate.

As we do not suggest the total abrogation of cheese and butter imports, however, what our argument comes to is this: that we ought to decrease our consumption of liquid milk, increase our production of butter, cheese, lard and pig-meat, increase the butter ration, abolish cheese rationing, maintain our milch herds at the existing figure or even increase them by reclaiming "rough grazing", but not if it can be shown that a higher meat production is more important.

There is one more point, however: that of cost.

The making of a pound of butter out of 2·348 gallons of milk costs about 2*s*. 4*d*. Liquid milk brings the farmer between 2*s*. and 3*s*. a gallon, and he is not overpaid at that figure by

[1] 264·1 gallons milk = 1 cwt. butter + butter-milk. 112·2 gallons milk = 1 cwt. cheese + whey, etc.

any means. Butter cannot possibly be fairly sold by the dairy-farmer—or his coöperative, for less than about 5*s.* 6*d.* or 6*s.* a pound. Whether this is paid by the public directly, or by a subsidy, will no doubt depend upon the politics of the Government in power at any given moment. But if we are to eat butter, that is the price we have to pay for it. And we ought to eat it.

BACON AND HAM

These foods have been dealt with in discussing barley and butter.

MEAT

What is the problem which we must solve to keep ourselves supplied with meat? Since, as we have already seen, we can get more food value out of our land by increasing cereal and, incidentally, intensively grown horticultural crops, at the expense of pasture, and since, in order to increase our home supply of butter and cheese, we do not want to reduce our head of milking cattle, it looks as if we are going to be badly off for meat.

Supposing this were to be the case, should we suffer in health? Probably not: vegetarians are, as a rule, healthy; but they are also, as a rule, not manual workers, which may be significant. As we have already pointed out, certain high civilizations have been virtually vegetarian, not, of course, on principle, but by force of circumstances. The Greeks of the heroic but relatively barbarous age were meat-eaters; the Athenians of the Great Age ate very little meat, subsisting largely on wheat, and for the same reason that we may be forced to do so: they could not feed their population off the soil of Attica, and the only food they could import in sufficient quantity was wheat. The great Asiatic agrarian cultures were not great meat-eaters, and the highly civilized series of societies which dwelt between the Rivers Maule and Ancasmayu in South America, and found their final social form as the beautifully ordered Inca communist state, had almost no meat, although here again their barbarous ancestors, or predecessors, were eaters of llama meat. But there is a point to be noted in this context: all the great societies which were vegetarian flourished in countries with a much higher sunshine-hours figure than Britain. Whether there is any significance in this we do not know: it is perhaps worth pointing out.

Socially and politically, there is another matter which should be taken into account in this connection. The student of any history which is not simply an account of kings, battles and treaties, notices that there is a kind of order of ferocity among mankind which, whether by chance or significantly, seems to be linked with diet. Briefly, it comes to this: when there is a clash between root-eating and cereal-eating folk, the root-eaters are invariably defeated. The manioc-eating South Americans were never able to stand up effectively to aggression by maize-eaters, for example. Moving up the scale, cereal-eaters seem to have been generally destroyed in war by meat-eaters. In the numerous clashes between pastoral and agrarian cultures—for example, that between the Aryan-speaking Wiros in India and the native Dasa or Dasyu—the meat-eaters triumph, as the Hyksos, the "Shepherd" people, were able to triumph over the Egyptian peasants. True, in the end, farmers come out best, and the shepherds and cowherds are beaten; but not until the originally conquered peasantry has absorbed the victorious culture and taken to eating meat.

Quite possibly, this apparent importance of diet is misleading. It may simply be that in more or less simple societies the cultivation of one kind of food rather than another is imposed by conditions which favour the growth of martial attributes among those people who have to work harder for their living. In that case, the diet factor would be of no significance in advanced societies. But it is worth bearing in mind, for we live in an age of political ferocity and need all our truculence to survive at all.

In considering, next, what meat we *can* afford to eat, let us begin by saying that we should, of course, continue to buy, principally from the Dominions, as much meat as we can fairly pay for without borrowing, and without forcing our merchandise by political or social arguments on reluctant markets. Quite apart from questions of pride and morality, we are seriously hampered in our own attempts to change and re-tool our industry to suit new economic patterns and the genius of our inventors and engineers, by the need to continue churning out old and not really profitable lines, e.g. calicoes, in order to buy food and raw materials at any price.

The principal meat-product of fine permanent pasture is beef. Mutton, pork and veal, or "baby beef", can be raised on less excellent grasses or more difficult sites. It is not possible—excepting on one condition—to increase the output of beef *and* butter and pork and bread. But, by increasing arable at the expense of pasture, and so raising our wheat output, we can also raise our pig population—as a super-by-product of dairy and grain farming—to such a figure that we might almost provide a quantity of pork equal to our total present meat ration. Pigs do not take up room, and it is room which is lacking. There is probably no technical reason why we should not multiply the pig population by ten. But to do it, we have to forgo beef—again, excepting on one condition, which we shall come to presently.

Mutton is another meat we could enormously increase without great difficulty, but to do it we might have to forgo a measure of specialization. The history of the sheep is not our subject, but it may be said that whereas, formerly, the sheep was a general-purpose animal, providing both wool and meat and even milk, it was subsequently the subject of much clever selection and breeding for special qualities. Sheep were bred and multiplied for fine wool or good mutton, not both, and, as a consequence, the more primitive animal is profitable in neither market. Naturally, it would be most undesirable and foolish to reverse this process. A gain in quality should never be given up. But there is only one reason why millions of half-wild sheep, cared for by shepherds, away from the farm, and not really treated as farm animals at all, should not be "run" in certain parts of mountain and moorland Britain. The claims of the shepherds on such sheep-runs would have to be reconciled with those of the Forestry Commission, but at all events, the domestic mutton supply *could* be raised, probably doubled, in a very few years, *provided*—and this is the only real condition—the price factor is completely disregarded. The price of such mutton must be calculated solely on its cost, so that a decent livelihood is assured to the shepherds. If this price is too high for the incomes of our people, then it must be paid by subsidy. We are simply not in a position, any longer, to dismiss any home food-producing device whatsoever as "uneconomic", unable to "compete". Compete for what? Profit? We do not, as a nation, want a profit. We want something to eat—and badly. We are going to be forced, like it or not, to pay whatever it costs to grow food at home, and the fact that it would be "cheaper" to manufacture motor-cars and stockings and sell them abroad for meat is becoming of merely academic interest—for the buyers of cars and stockings grow fewer and fewer, while our hunger remains.

There is, in Britain today, a constant waste of meat through the killing, in infancy, of unwanted bull calves. If the farmer has the means to feed the calf for the six months which will turn it into "baby beef", he will have to take a loss when he sells the carcase. So he sells it—for potted meat or some industrial use—at a few weeks of age. Here again, the development of a hill-pastures farming for the feeding of bull calves for veal and "baby beef" would, and could, almost without delay, enhance our meat ration; and again the only argument against it is that it does not "pay". What cynical nonsense this business of "paying" is, in a world increasingly short of food! Unless, indeed, we are all so sick of life that we should be glad to starve to death, as a few thousand Asiatics have done since we began to write this chapter, then food is worth whatever it costs, and our whole economy must be adjusted to that simple and irrefutable fact.

If we are not to rely for independence in meat supply, and for an increase in the meat ration, only upon a very great change in our diet, in favour of pork, mutton and baby beef, then, once again, as throughout this chapter, we must turn to our "rough grazing" and moorland, our bad lands and our reclaimable estuaries.

Even those men, to whom we are and shall continue to be deeply indebted, who, like Dr. Stamp, have studied and written and spoken in an indefatigable attempt to get us to pay attention to our wasted land, have tended to treat this problem of bad-land reclamation in a far too moderate spirit. They want to see such land cleared, ploughed and brought to a higher state of fertility, and therefore productivity, by orthodox means. They do not seem to regard such land as capable of being re-made by us, until it becomes as good as the best.

But this is what we must do; and there is no doubt that it can be done. Only, it would entail a major social and economic revolution. But why not make up our minds to make that revolution *deliberately*, beginning now and proceeding in an orderly fashion, instead of either gradually falling into a lower and lower category among the economically and physically depressed nations, or, alternatively, being suddenly and terribly faced with famine and starvation?

Level land, however bad, can be re-made. It is a matter for scientists and engineers, who must be provided with the means. What means? Ample money, ample machinery, ample labour and ample materials. Clearance and levelling, draining, are all manageable on a vast scale by machinery. Much more difficult is the bringing to life of "dead" gravel and rank clay. It can be provided with nutrients easily enough, by the use (not the abuse, however) of fertilizers. But to become good soil it must be made open, loose, crumbly to a considerable depth. This can be done by two methods, supplementing each other. By the use of the new synthetic polyuranide and polysaccharide resins as soon as they become available in quantity. And, better, by composting wastes on a really vast scale. Impossible? Not at all; merely costly. *We cannot afford it*—so say the orthodox economists who still fancy themselves in a half-empty world, full of industrious peasants cultivating virgin soils and anxious to buy our goods. The truth is—we cannot *avoid* affording it—unless we would rather starve, of course.

Let us, at the risk of being tedious, re-state the simple problem. Rising world population is consuming shrinking world food supplies. Britain, importing half her food, was once a world public benefactor. She is becoming increasingly a world liability: a public nuisance, a poor relation. Britain has about 50 million acres of land not yet built on or otherwise "sterilized". Of this, 24 million acres are good land. Off 24 million acres she can, by intensive high farming, feed about 24 million people. If the 50 million acres were all as productive as the best land, she could feed her population. She must face, very soon, the necessity of feeding that population, or most of it. What is to be done? Make all our land good land. Can it be done? Why not? A score of ancient peoples did it, without one hundredth part of our technical resources.

We hear much of the great powers of science, the great benefits conferred by it. Hitherto, alas, the most spectacular, although not the most important, achievements of science have been destructive. This is not the fault of the scientists; it is our fault.

We are certain that if we, the nation, say to them, our scientific fellow citizens—engineers, botanists, agronomists, ecologists, biologists, physicists, chemists *and* farmers—if we say to them, "Here are millions of money and hands. We will get you the materials you want. Now, make our 25 million acres of marginal land, bad land, mountain land, into soil as fertile and deep as our best,"—they can and will do it.

Why do we waste our hills and mountains when Stone Age peoples lived by terrace agriculture? That is only one of fifty such questions we could ask. The answer, of course, is that we are still thinking of our world as infinitely and inexhaustibly provided with potential food in fertile and easily farmed soil. It is not true; and even if it were, we, the British, could no longer buy our share of it.

What has all this to do with beef? This much: that bad-land reclamation would probably begin by the making of deep-rooted leys on the reconstituted soils, and these we could stock with beef cattle which would carry forward the work of soil-making, while providing us with beef. Subsequently, no doubt, these new soils would become alternately arable for cereal and root culture, and arable pasture for mowing or for grazing.

We *can* have beef: we can eat heartily. It will cost us a few factories, a large number of bad and obsolete social and economic habits, and a vast amount of money. But this money will be capital invested, not income squandered, and it will be paid to British manufacturers and British labour and British farmers—so that we shall, as a nation, simply be taking it out of one pocket and putting it into the other.

FISH

Of fish, we need say nothing. If increased supplies are called for, it is a matter of increased fishing, limited by the numbers of fish in the sea, which are no more inexhaustible than soil fertility.

EGGS AND POULTRY

We want not less than 1 million tons of eggs a year from native poultry—that is, double our actual output. And poultry, as meat, is a form of livestock we are very well equipped, in some respects, to keep in vastly greater numbers than we now do. Any significant increase in this source of two of the best foods, however, depends on the possibility of another increase, already discussed, in grain acreage. We could grow maize in southern Britain, but there is probably no advantage in doing so, since the yield of other grains per acre is as high or higher, and wheat, as a food, is superior to maize.

Like pigs, poultry, with the exception of geese, are food-processing rather than food-making animals. Geese are grazers, but as such compete with cattle and sheep. Chickens are grazers to a small extent, but they are foraging animals: there are three principal ways of keeping them. As domestic or cottage animals, like pigs, they can be fed to a considerable extent on household food wastes. The Village Produce Association and other bodies are encouraging the keeping of domestic poultry which could and should be far more numerous than they are.

As waste-consumers, chickens are more valuable to us, in our circumstances, than as specialized food-processing machines kept in batteries and fed largely on imported foods. As farm-yard scroungers they are very valuable, since, although they have to be fed, they pick up a large part of their living for themselves, eliminating waste of dropped grain. Again, as foraging birds, kept in open fields with cattle, they collect for us—since we eat their eggs or their carcases—a great deal of animal food not otherwise viable for our own consumption—grubs, insects, worms and other nourishing but unpalatable small creatures.

On the whole, it seems likely that we could greatly increase our egg production, and that we could best afford to do it by keeping far more back-yard, farmyard and field poultry, rather than by increasing battery poultry-farming. It is true that the increase in the eggs-per-bird figure would be far smaller than if we established more specialized poultry farms. But the increased feeding requirement would be such as we can find without much difficulty.

FRUIT

Three hundred and thirty-two thousand of our acres are devoted to growing fruit, and farmers are frequently urged to plant more. But it does not always pay them to do so because whereas, in a bad season, an insignificant crop robs them of any return on the acres "invested" in fruit, in a good year almost no steps are taken to absorb the glut. Yet, in 1951, we imported 968,000 tons of fruit, more than half of it, however, such as we cannot grow here.

There can be no question at all that we could in Britain grow the whole supply of temperate-climate fruits required by our population, including grapes and peaches. All the technical problems have been solved. But not the economic problems. Fruit plantations well run do not even engross completely the land occupied by the trees and shrubs, excepting cherries and perhaps plums, which cannot be intercropped excepting during their early years. But where really intensive horticulture is practised, as in the Benelux countries, apples, pears, gooseberries and currants can be intercropped with vegetables and flowers, and the soil bears two, three or four crops. In Northern Italy it is common to see maize and wheat fields separated by hedges of peaches and grapes, which in Britain could be apples, pears and raspberries. We simply have no idea of getting the most out of our soil, not because our horticulturists lack skill and enthusiasm, but because they lack capital and encouragement.

What steps should be taken to increase home supplies of fruit and eliminate imports of all but tropical and sub-tropical fruits?

First, an absolute assurance that the total crop will be sold every year. The best way to do this would be the establishment of regional fruit-growers' buying-and-selling coöperatives which would, themselves, be members of Central Coöperative Marketing and Purchasing Boards in all the great centres of population. These organizations would be non-profit-earning. They would advance money to growers, against the subsequent crop; they would collect and sell the fruit; they would buy packing and other marketing material for their members; they would represent their members with official and Governmental bodies; they would also have a share in deciding the fruit-import policy. Finally, and most important, they would own and operate means of preserving and using glut fruit crops.

This is important, because at the moment we wantonly waste immense quantities of fruit.

We will deal with only a simple example. One of the noblest achievements of our welfare society has been that of supplying expectant and nursing mothers and their infants with vitamin supplements. Of the three most important vitamins, A and D are plentiful in black currants, and in fact in many fruits, including apples and oranges. Originally, black currants were used by the Government as a source of these vitamins. Later, imported oranges were used. Why? We cannot grow oranges; we can very easily grow all the black currants we need. Oranges cost foreign currency, most of it hard. As for apples—the situation is a disgrace and a scandal. No less an authority than Mr. Raymond Bush has not hesitated to suggest, in print, that the attempt to make proper use of English apple juice was foiled by the influence of the synthetic soft-drinks industry. Nothing is more likely.

We import, annually, half a million tons of oranges and vast numbers of apples. We waste, annually, not less than 100,000 tons, and probably 250,000 tons of home-grown apples. We could, without the slighest difficulty or inconvenience:

(1) Eliminate apple and pear imports.

(2) Grow and gas-store all the apples and pears we can eat.

(3) Reduce orange or orange-juice imports by making and bottling apple juice, equally delicious and nutritious, of all sub-grade apples.

(4) Use apple juice and black currant juice as a vitamin supplement welfare food, instead of orange juice.

But this is not all: one of the worst vices of industrialism is that of fobbing-off the "lower income groups" with rubbishy foods. It is very well known that our factory jams are made with nameless pulps, preservatives, and sugar substitutes. It should be and must be illegal to use anything whatsoever but fresh, home-grown fruit and sugar to make jam. Our horticulture can, and readily will, supply all the soft fruit the nation can eat. But it must be capitalized, organized and secure, and it must be fairly paid for its product.

We repeat once again: real food is worth what it costs.

One of the almost incredible follies of the past few years has been the exporting of tin-plate to fruit-canning countries, leaving our own fruit-canning industry so short of supplies that millions of tons of home-grown fruit has been wasted, has rotted on the ground where it fell. Fruit-canning must be controlled by fruit-growers, through their coöperatives. And it must become a crime, heavily punishable, to waste fruit crops! If we can more than we eat or need to store—splendid! We shall export canned fruit to several countries and earn, instead of squandering, money.

Plum-growing in Britain is subject to climatic conditions which make the crop vary widely from year to year. In glut years, there are too many plums. They can and should be bought—in case of re-organization of horticulture on the lines suggested, by the growers' coöperatives—and dried. Home-dried prunes are expensive? Rubbish! Home-grown fruit is, for a nation in our situation, *never* expensive, even if it has to be subsidized because industrial wages are too low.

It should be made clear that in return for capital and security, horticulture must supply quality, that market-gardening and orcharding must be subject to control, and that the wastage of orchard land by undercropping, by the growing of inferior varieties and by technical backwardness, will not be tolerated. The nation cannot afford it. Every fruit tree in Britain must be the very best variety the soil and climate of the region will support, and while growers should be helped to replace inferior orchards, they will, in return, be obliged to supply superior crops.

SUGAR

As we noticed in Chapter III, we produce a fifth of our sugar consumption. In view of the demands which sugar-beet makes on land, it might, until recently, have been difficult to justify the suggestion that we ought to increase the acreage under this crop, at present about 425,000. Such an increase can only be obtained at the expense of other crops. Moreover, there is a world glut of sugar and the sugar-growing West Indies are distressed.

A new factor, however, is the value of sugar-beet tops for cattle-feed. We now know that an acre of sugar beet produces three crops at once: the tops, or leaves, which, made into silage, provide winter feed for cattle, and therefore can, within certain limits, be regarded as replacement for other fodder crops; the roots, for the extraction of sugar; and the residual pulp, which is also quite good food for cattle. Thus, sugar beet is a valuable crop and our farmers would be justified in growing a greater acreage of it, at the expense of other fodder crops. It is, however, as futile for them to do so as for fruit-growers to plant more and better orchards, until industry catches up with agriculture; until, in short, the industrial plant to process the crop exists.

H. J. Massingham

CHAPTER V

The Use of Land

IT SHOULD be clear from Chapters III and IV that an industrial system which, like our own, has got out of hand is bound both to misuse and abuse the land. The examples we have given are not a chapter of accidents, errors and mishandlings in certain regions. They are inherent in the structure of an overwhelmingly urban civilization. It is inevitable that a nation, committing itself to feeding a vast factory proletariat and highly organized services of every kind and type, and accomplishing this Herculean task by an equally complicated mechanism of exchanging exports and planting investments in return for bulk-imports of cheap foreign food, should neglect its own countryside. The agricultural depressions from the 'sixties of last century to the Repeal of the Corn Production Act in the 'twenties of our own have not been bolts from the blue, but determined, as night follows day. A nation engaged in international cut-throat trade competition can do no other than put the factory before the home farm and draw off the rural population into it. It is equally bound to exploit its own land when that land ceases to be the source of its fundamental needs. Much of it will be regarded as mere ground, mere space for expansion, and it is the nature of an industrial state to expand. It is no less certain to replace the idea of a countryside as the primary province of man's life and work, by the novel conception of it as a playground. When the majority of people live in towns, they look upon the country as a recreation but, as most of them visit it in hordes, they bring the town mentality with them.

But that is not the whole of the story. Since industry for the manipulation of raw materials is the core of an industrial state and the city is dominant in all national functions and activities, agriculture must play second fiddle to them. Its own methods, observations, traditions, developed—it is not too much to say—out of an intimate friendship with the land, must give place to urban and industrial ideas of how land should be farmed. Hence, in our own time we have the spectacle of the industrialization of agriculture by applying to it purely commercial standards, by considering the power of the machine as superior to the skill of hands, and engineering and chemical agents as superior to organic ones. The mechanist, the chemist and the engineer can and should all play their part in the reconstruction of agriculture; but not that of a master and a dictator who laughs at the laws of nature. This domination greatly affects the use of agricultural land, quite apart from its misuse, because it represents a clash between urban and rural values in which the latter stand no chance at all. You cannot make the best use of land without studying the way that nature works—ecology again. Moreover, one of the fixed illusions of an industrial nation is that natural resources are inexhaustible, a fallacy that leads straight to famine.

Lastly, from these data has emerged a kind of philosophy, that of "the conquest of nature". Such a point of view not only twists an associate into an enemy, but arbitrarily creates a deep and wide division between man and nature. Of course, there are reactions against the presumption of this attitude—in the passion for gardens, in numerous books about country life, in what is called "primitive" farming, in the new biological farming school advocating the return of all wastes to the soil, and so on. Nevertheless, it remains true that to speak of "the love of nature" is an anomaly in these "scientific" days; for what you genuinely love, you respect and refrain from misusing for your own ends.

Such a philosophy begins at the wrong end in approaching the complex question of the right use of land. It is probable that this scientific war against nature was first declared in T. H. Huxley's famous Romanes Lecture, in which he contrasted the moral forces of mankind with the apish and tigerish disorder of the cosmic scheme from which man was descended. Actually, the ferocious trade-competition of the Victorian era was far more tigerish than the rivalry in the most savage of jungles, and there can be little doubt that Huxley quite unconsciously translated the conditions of the age in which he lived into his reading of the natural world. The next step was to drop out the moral element and to continue the battle for conquest as between technical man and the impersonal forces of nature. As a result, the pundits sometimes betray an astonishing ignorance of "the laws of nature" in their zeal to impose their own mechanistic interpretation upon them.

Therefore, there is no point in considering the proper use of land if agriculture be regarded merely as a technical means to an expedient end. In other words, we cannot use our heritage of land for the purpose of supporting ourselves from it, without a drastic change of mind, change of heart and change of method towards it. We cannot become good stewards of our land so that it may respond to the urgency of our needs, without some kind of conversion. To rely solely upon the engineer and the technologist as instruments for exorcizing the spectre of famine would be merely to aggravate the situation that has brought us to the verge of it. Our technical equipment will come in very handy, but we can no longer allow it to rule the roost.

Fortunately, we have, as Wordsworth said, "great allies" in the process of conversion, and perhaps the most potent of them is sheer necessity, a more persuasive teacher than a library of arguments and a host of orators. Nor, if we have mislaid our ancestral memory, can we have entirely destroyed it. If we are on the point of failure as an over-urbanized society after 150 years of it, we did pretty well as an agricultural one for twice 1,500 years. We possess an equable climate not subject to extremes, and soils which, if not quite so fertile as when Tull, Coke and Townshend were making their experiments in the 18th century, are nothing like so depleted as in America,

Africa, Australia and elsewhere. If we were able to produce 75% of our own food during the last war without the proper complement of men and by extractive methods, our acres are capable of producing 100% of it in a fully manned countryside and by a truly ecological system of reclamation, conservation and good management.

We should, then, regard the stopping of food supplies from abroad as an event which would only temporarily dislocate the national life and expose it only for the time being to a variety of perils and hardships. Indeed, we should think of it as a great release from an abnormal situation which robbed the land of capital, the farmers of their due reward as producers, the people as a whole of a proper nutrition in their food and much of the countryside of its beauty and peace.

Such a change-over should also be welcomed as a supreme opportunity for the people as a whole to lead a more normal and natural life; for great numbers of workers, thrown out of employment by the breakdown of the industrial system of exchange, to be engaged upon all manner of recreative works in the countryside; for a true economy to replace an obsolete economics. We should think of it as opening the door to a new life, hard enough but also inspiriting by its constructive and redeeming purpose. The old system was a vicious one because it depended on exploiting the foreign farmer in the interests of cheapness and profiteering, depressing the home farmer by unjust prices for his produce, and the factory worker by low wages. When the bottom falls out of a trade which exports manufactures in return for inferior food, at least the nation is relieved from the perpetual see-saw of booms and slumps. And is it a bad or a good thing that the cities should be thinned of their unhealthy deposits of fat? Which in the long run is the saner life, that of the plough or the conveyor belt? That of a landless proletariat or a landed, responsible and independent community of primary producers?

*

Hitherto, the story of our land has been the first part of Cinderella's. In order to bring our story to as gratifying a conclusion as the traditional one, we must undertake a gigantic task, which may be divided into three parts—to reclaim waste-land, to restore misapplied land, and both to replenish the fertility and to intensify the production of existing farmland. There can be no doubt that so formidable a triple undertaking cannot be achieved without overhauling our administrative machinery. The first step to that end is surely to rearrange our entire food-bearing acreage upon a regional basis; and nothing could be more regional than the structure and surface of our native land. Not only is each region of it distinct in vegetation, rock-formation, landscape, rainfall and sometimes even in climate, but this natural diversity of characteristics extends to individual fields. Diversity of land means elasticity in farming it, and "the parish", as Æ. wrote, "is the cradle of the nation". This regional differentiation is essential for what seems a paradoxical reason—namely, to enable us to cope adequately with the land as a whole, or rather a series of wholes bound together into a greater whole.

Notice how we deal with the land when it is not marked off, as it ought to be, into its appropriate regions. Government legislation for agriculture is almost invariably piecemeal and hand-to-mouth; it concentrates now on one crop, now on another; it is all for corn one day and cattle the next, not for a balanced system of crop and animal husbandry. The object is to prop up the tottering structure by a new buttress when it sways in the wind of crisis, not to rebuild its foundations nor even to underpin them. Specialization from office and laboratory has reached such a pitch of minute subdivision that not only does knowledge become more and more about less and less, but coördination between its interacting parts breaks down completely. This is the industrial way but it is certainly not the way of the good farmer or of the natural landscape he farms. Only by the regional approach can the parts be observed as integral to the whole.

For it will not be monoculture in the American style that will save us from famine.

The man who studies the interrelations of these parts and tries to understand the whole through them is the ecologist. Therefore in the programme of regenerating the land and recharging it with fertility, he ought to come first. Dr. Pfeiffer, the Dutch ecologist, has in his book, *The Earth's Face*, made the suggestion that man's stewardship of the earth can only be made effective by the appointment of Land Wardens—we would add Regional Land Wardens, each with his staff and responsible to a new central Ministry of Lands. The latter proposition comes from Sir George Stapledon, and the idea of the Land Warden is implicit in the late Christopher Turnor's references[1] to a County Land Development and Fertility Committee. This is a much clumsier title than that of Regional Land Warden but means much the same thing, except that "region" is closer to the natural land-surface than "county".

The first consideration of a Regional Land Warden would be the fertility of all the interacting parts in his particular region. The necessary funds would be supplied by the Ministry of Land, but plans on a smaller scale might be financed by grants from such a body as the Development Commission which already issues them for farming experiments.

The existence of these Land Wardens would be a guarantee in itself that the pernicious term "uneconomic" had become meaningless. It is a purely financial valuation. It is opposed to basing a true economy upon the resources of the land, instead of upon the state of the export market, the variations in the exchange rates or the manipulations of dealers. From nothing has agriculture and the land itself suffered more than from the fluctuations whereby sheep, for instance, have become "uneconomic" in one decade and "economic" in the next. Crop or stock is "uneconomic" if it fails to fit into the industrial pattern, while the capital reserves of the soil are treated as income. The business of a Land Warden would be to advise

[1] *op. cit.*

the farmer on all the issues relating to the maintenance of his farm's fertility—shelter belts, rotations, mixed stocking, the proper balance between crop and stock and so on—and to report to the Ministry in all cases where they were infringed. His concern would be not with production in itself but the conditions necessary to the organic health of the farm as a whole.

Here is one example chosen at random from many potential ones, and already mentioned in Chapter IV. Specialization of dairying produce has reduced cheese- and butter-making in this country to next to nothing. But the extravagant "export" of liquid milk in our dairying is a form of monoculture resulting in the loss of calcium and phosphates. Butter-making takes from 2 to 3 gallons of milk per lb., but cheese-making hardly one. Once every English county made its own local brand of cheese. In both butter- and cheese-making the whey and all the minerals are returned to the land via the pigs and the calves, and so this deficiency is redressed. Hence, the Land Warden would advocate one or both, to the benefit not only of the farm, but of the consumer, to whom liquid milk is a natural food in childhood, but *not in adulthood*.

But, of course, the Land Warden's responsibilities would not be confined to the farm in isolation from its setting, its natural environment. If this were in ecological disorder, the farm itself would suffer. Equally within the province of a Land Warden's duties would be to supervise the reclaiming of waste or derelict land, to see that the land was kept in good ecological order and to assess to what extent abused land was capable of being handed back to agriculture. He should also be empowered to advise the prohibition of land-use for non-agricultural development when it is good land and well farmed or where such development would split up the local integrity of the district. The Town and Country Planning Act is only remotely concerned with ecology, which, by the way, is the foundation of beauty in landscape. His criterion in many aspects of land-restoration would be the excellent work of the

U.S.A. Soil Conservation Service. He would thus be a very important figure indeed to a nation struggling into self-sufficiency and he should never be embarrassed for funds, whether for himself, his staff or his work. The difficulty might well be the *personnel*. We have made such a mess of our land, and ecology is still so novel an art or science or both, that the trained ecologist is a rare bird. In our fragmented world, the expert who knows everything about the fraction of a whole, vastly outnumbers the ecologist who makes a biological study of the whole itself. In our fantastic economics the specialist is the best, and the all-rounder the worst, paid. But only the ecologist can teach us by degrees that agriculture is *not* an "industry", as nearly everybody calls it—even reformers like Stapledon and others—but a livelihood, a stewardship, a trust and the foundation of the national life.

Whether the County Agricultural Committees should survive into a new era of intensive farming and the reclamation of waste land is questionable. If their membership possessed such qualifications to advise and guide the farming community as does the Kentish one, there could be no doubt as to the answer. Unfortunately, this is not so, and some of the Committees acquired a bad reputation during the last war for stupidity, despotism and unjust dispossession. "Inefficiency" has been too often the watchword for penalizing the farmer. Mere economic efficiency *may* sometimes be, but more often is not by any means, a yard-stick for good husbandry. But the Committees are at any rate a body of producers themselves, and were they to be subordinate to the Land Wardens and the best of the smaller farmers admitted to them, the answer should be *yes*. As for the N.A.A.S. (National Advisory Agricultural Service), composed as it mostly is of orthodox economists and specialists, the dons of the farming world and isolated from it, the question is whether a nation painfully learning bedrock farming can possibly afford such an expensive luxury. Perhaps it can, but its worth and influence should be offset by its direct opposite—namely an English adaptation of such European bodies as the Provincial Peasant Farmers' Association. Indeed, the Ministry of Agriculture itself would be in closer *rapport* with the farmers if its higher officials (not to mention the lower) had for a background some practical experience on the land.

For the all-important question of locally developed land-use, the utmost encouragement ought to be given to local Producers' Marketing Boards and to coöperative buying and selling societies serving both local producers and consumers. One such group already exists—the independent Village Produce Associations, which take in hundreds of villages and whose main object is for each village to become self-supporting on its own home produce throughout the year. The Associations bulk-buy their own seeds, stock, fodder, lime, etc., give the small producer a voice, organize shows, foster storing and preserving, and are a link between the gardener, the Women's Institutes and such stock-keeping bodies as the Small Pig-keepers' Council. The V.P.A.s might well become, too, a nucleus for the revival of village crafts, especially when every village in the land joins them. The Associations bear directly upon the issue of land-use, since they make every effort to teach villagers good husbandry. As for the rural de-population which is one of the main causes for the misuse of land, the Land Settlement Association has an important part to play in reversing this trend, but it must first free itself from the mistakes it owes to the politicians.

*

The drawback of this chapter is that the subject of land-use is too vast for us to penetrate far into the interior. So, for want of space we must leave the problem of administration. It is closely allied to that of finance, and finance has bedevilled our whole economic system by confusing money with real wealth, with the result that we consume more of the latter than we produce. We imagine that such wealth as food-supply can be cured of shortages simply by handing over more money to its buyer, an illusion that has inflated the £1 at the cost of deflating real wealth. The commercial farmer gets more and more tangled up with the costliness of his farming in machinery, fertilizers and labour. The latter he, like everybody else, calls "man-power", as though a man were merely a unit of energy, while the man-power itself is absorbed in higher wages, shorter hours and easier work, because its idea of wealth is in terms of money instead of land-worth, while fertility, the most vital asset of real wealth, is depreciated by money-pressure. The standards of commercialism tend always to be financial, earnings and profits, the increase of which are almost invariably at the expense of the sources of real wealth—land-fertility and human skill.

It could not be otherwise, therefore, than that finance has played havoc with our available land. Can you wonder at it, when the grossest disparity has for so long nourished the distributor at the expense of the producer? Before the last war producers received £500,000,000 a year, while a further £682,000,000, of costs were added by processing, transport and distribution. This disparity is certainly no less today. Turnor gives an example of swedes bought at £2 a ton and sold for £18. In the competition, again, between food prices at home and abroad, it has been the importer's goods which have caused those of the home-market to sink below the cost of production. We know of a shocking case in 1948: one of the best fruit-farmers in England was forced by foreign competition to sell his entire crop of dessert pears and apples to Bulmer's in Hereford for perry and cider at a penny a pound. A dealer's civilization is as destructive as it is ignorant of the permanent value of land.

Another flagrant example of discrimination between primary agriculture and secondary industry has been the *ad valorem* duty the importer paid after the nominal abolition of Free Trade in 1931, 10% if the imports were for industry, 25% if for agriculture. It is probable that no land in the world is so under-capitalized as our own, and between 1929 and 1939 agriculture lost £255,000,000 in capital. Food-subsidies have provided a helping hand, but not so much to the producer as to the consumer. Thus in innumerable instances has money been promoted from the servant of real wealth, to its master.

It is an astonishing thing that in this country there is no adequate land-purchase system, while farms can be bought only at fantastic prices. But for an occasional exception here and there which proves the rule, there is no provision of credit, as abroad, without, or at a very low rate of, interest—long-term credit for reclamation work and short-term to augment the farmer's working capital. If he has to borrow, he goes nine times out of ten to the bank; that is to say, he increases his overdraft (overdrafts in 1939 amounted to £60,000,000 and today the figure is about £200,000,000). Nor is there any sinking fund to enable him to pay off the loan. Under the Agricultural Credits Act of 1928, the rate of interest was left to the Banks. Without stabilizing prices at equitable levels and abandoning usury in order to return to the long-forgotten concept of the "just price", farming remains a Cinderella, with trafficking in its double sense as her two ugly sisters.

Death duties, again, are entirely undiscriminating; like the rain, they fall upon the just and the unjust alike, upon the landowner who farms his own land and applies an ecological conscience to his estate, as upon the landowner who turns his land into a pheasant reserve. We even encourage the bad landholder by calling the small farm "uneconomic", when we do nothing to prevent a company director acquiring a farm or estate in order, by misfarming it and running it at a loss, to evade income tax in his urban business. We allow many of our farms to be owned by companies or corporations, as though they were factories, instead of by individual farmers; or permit one man to own two or more farms which, as George Henderson[1] has said, he no more needs than two dinners. It is true that a multiple owner like Lord Iveagh on the Suffolk Brecks, some of the poorest land in England, has more than justified his ownership of thousands of acres, as Lord Tollemache in the

[1] *Farmer's Progress* (Faber, 1950).

last century more than justified his. But one or two swallows don't make a summer.

To such an extent does finance dominate the farm at the expense of proper land-use that by the Agricultural Holdings Act of 1908 the old Tenancy Agreements, whereby the land was safeguarded from exploitation, were abolished and the tenant was given the right to sell hay and straw off his farm, a process almost as detrimental to its fertility as taking three corn-crops in succession off one field, which he is now entitled to do. These are, of course, only a few examples of obstruction to proper land-use by a mischievous finance, and it is evident that a self-supporting Britain, which cannot be achieved without a fertile land put to the best and fullest service, must devise a new financial economy to irrigate such service. Instead of basing the monetary system upon the shadowy gold-reserves hoarded in Fort Knox, we have to anchor it upon the most solid, permanent and indispensable of all our possessions—the land itself, under the present system a wasted asset. The most fundamental economic structure is the land and the most fundamental economic activity the conservation and cultivation of it.

The revision of the educational system is of even greater importance than that of finance and administration. It is not enough to tell people what to do and to find them the wherewithal to do it; we must change their mentality from a window-box one into a field one. We shall say little about education here, since it is dealt with in another chapter. But it bears upon the subject of land-use for the simple reason that our country children are ceasing to possess any land sense whatever. How should they develop it, when the smaller village schools are all closed and they are carried off in buses to the larger ones? Most of the curriculum of such schools and the whole of the examination system attached to it are so overwhelmingly urban in bias that their effect is not to educate their pupils in rural life, but train them to get out of it. So long as a smattering of standardized book-learning and pouring liquids into test-tubes are considered as a higher form of culture than thatching a rick, rearing a calf or driving a straight furrow, or even maintaining a tractor; so long as boys receive the impression that a black coat is superior wear to a rough jacket and corduroys, and girls regard the typist and telephone operator as a higher type of being than the cook, or the dairymaid—so long will schools be incubators of false values. Well has Stapledon warned our generation of its pathetic confidence in the pundit and the text-book. Only by reversing this de-naturing process can children hope to be initiated into country-mindedness and so to find their livelihood in the country places where they were born.

To that end, not only should the smaller schools universally run their own gardens and the bigger ones (including the public schools) their own farms, but the school should be the first rung of the ladder, apprenticeship the second and the acquisition of a farm the third and top. At present, there is neither the wood nor the will to construct such a ladder, the landless labourer having no more chance to obtain his own farm than have his son or daughter at school to acquire the rudiments of a land-sense. Fortunately for us, we have before us the perfect example of organically relating the school to the land—namely, the Danish Folk High Schools, schools which link land-sense with literature, the arts and the sciences in the spirit of a true culture.

In the 19th century, Denmark was carved up into huge *latifundia*. These were all but ruined by tariffs and imported wheat. Hence the country turned from large-scale extensive, to small-scale intensive farming, with the result that, whereas our own country in 1938 was accommodating 334 farms of over 1,000 acres, in Denmark today there are 70 cultivators per 1,000 acres. The instrument in this act of conversion was the Danish Folk High School. But the vital issue of re-populating the land by means of peasant holdings must be left to future chapters.

*

The reclamation of land which has degenerated into artificial waste opens the programme of recovery because, as with drainage schemes and the like, it calls for the employment of multitudes of unskilled labourers. What other work will be available, what else can they do when the export trade collapses? Reclamation will also cost a great deal of money to nation, group and individual. But a nation which has not scrupled to spend £300,000,000 a year on imported food can afford, by a new system of issuing money, to meet the needs involved in putting its own land in order. Land-use means effective cultivation, and the more intensive it is, the more workers it demands. The restoration of marginal lands includes the regulation of the rivers, since their catchment areas are nearly always situated in moorland, hill and mountain country.

Without doubt the steeper and more exposed slopes, especially when they face north, ought to be re-afforested, not with pit-props, for reasons already given, but mixed and deciduous forest. Some of the southern foot-hills—in the Middle Wye Valley, for instance, where the climate is benign and the rainfall moderate—might well be terraced to make prolific gardens of soft fruit and the choicer vegetables. Where the hills of the North and West are ploughable for oats, potatoes or seed-mixtures, contour-ploughing across the slope should be the rule, a rule never practised in Britain because it would overturn the tractor. But not the horse, and there is room in a regenerate Britain for re-introducing limited numbers of horses especially on small farms, and for their value in doing odd jobs on larger ones. Besides, a contour-ploughing tractor is not an impossibility. Up-and-down ploughing in hill country is an invitation to erosion.

It is impossible to over-estimate the star-part played by hanging forests, not merely as wind-breaks and shelter-belts for farms (farm and forest have been arbitrarily divorced in our time), but in controlling the flow of rivers, supplying the springs, sponging the soil, softening the climate, conditioning the rainfall and keeping the very skin of the earth in good health.[1] The more ecologically-minded among authorities believe that at least one-third of our marginal lands ought to be re-afforested. How little we are concerned with the incalculable value of the mixed woodland today is shown by our thriftlessness in not planting groups of trees in odd corners and on small units of wasteland, of which there must be millions! And how unworthy are we of our past in felling wholesale the timber planted so zealously by our forefathers! Not only do we over-fell, but we allow the surviving trees to be slowly throttled to death by ivy or to exclude the light by growing into one another, by knocking nails into hedgerow timber, permitting dead limbs to rot the boles and so on. We no longer understand the elements of selective felling such as we have seen the all-but-obsolete chairleg bodgers of the Chilterns practise, while the finest of all foresters in planting trees the right distance apart and in the right proximity of one species to another—the jay—we destroy as a pest. Conquer not nature, as Pfeiffer truly said, but the robber economics which is preparing for us a starving planet.

It is not commonly realized that the Scottish Highlands have suffered as much from exploitation as from negligence; the forests by smelting, the hill-lands by the big sheep-farms of "the Clearances", the fisheries by steam-trawlers and, in the most modern developments, the river-network by hydro-electric power. It is impossible to restore the family croft, the natural and immemorial unit of Scottish agriculture, without rebuilding the depleted fertility of its land and the fisheries as a part-time occupation (excessive rainfall hinders full-time farming) of the crofter, not to mention clearing the bracken. Much, too, could be done in stimulating the birth-rate of table-fishes in the freshwater lochs by composting them, at present an experiment in its infancy. All our mountain lands need reclamation on the grand scale, not only for their own sakes, but because hill-country is the key to the fertility of plains and

[1] See John Stuart Collis's *The Triumph of the Tree* (Cape, 1950).

valleys. Only a generous expenditure of State money can achieve this object, but the reclaimed lands should be held on easy terms, subject to strict conditions as to proper land-use, by the individual farmer. The dilapidation of farmsteads as a consequence of the flight from the remoter areas would alone cost a pretty penny.

If sheep in the Highlands have eliminated the sweeter grasses and the forest seedlings, it is not because there are too many of them but because, being out of balance with cattle, they become a form of monoculture. Nor can sheep alone hold the bracken, since the heaviest hooves of cattle and horses are needed to crush the young fronds as they appear. Mr. Moses Griffiths of Aberystwyth has worked out a constructive proposal for re-stocking 5 million acres of rehabilitated marginal land with 1 million store cattle for summer grazing and for annually rearing on the hills 400,000 calves which would be fattened on the lowlands. This, he declares, would increase the supply of home-produced beef by 80,000 tons a year. He advocates another 10 million sheep ("Progress Report"[1] put the figure at 5 million) whose output, he claims, would be 60,000 tons a year of mutton and lamb. He further suggests an eight-year rotation of roots and seed-mixtures, both for the breeding flock and the herds, with dressings of lime and basic slag. Ten years is the limit he gives for his broad-based plan to become operative. The experiment of Lord Lovat among the mountains of Glen Strathfarrar has revealed how speedily the more edible grasses re-appear when a sizeable head of cattle is pastured on them. In three years, heather and bracken were cropped down so effectively that the grasses seized their chances of coming through.

It has been said that grass is the most important crop in the world, and Sir George Stapledon has dealt at length with the possibilities of re-seeding permanent pasture and rough grazings relapsed into mat-grass, blue grass, heather, bracken or scrub, with kidney vetches, cocksfoot, clovers, rye grass, sheep's

[1] Chapter IV.

fescue and others of the more nutritious grasses. How essential it is to re-condition deteriorated pastures may be gathered from the figures given by Dr. Stamp[1] as to the need of reducing permanent grass by the plough from nearly 19 million acres to 14 million, and rough grazings from almost the same acreage to 8,450,000. Leys, whether short or long, are, of course, familiar farming practice, but their mixtures are rarely numerous and deep-rooted enough to include a wider variety of grasses, together with deep-rooting herbs to tap the minerals and trace elements of the subsoil. Hence, the not uncommon spectacle of cattle turning up their nostrils at what seems a rich sward and making pell-mell for the ditches and hedgerows to devour the lowly but medicinal weeds. It may be added that heavy stocking on good grass has been facilitated of recent years by the useful invention of the daily-moved electric fence, especially for small areas of meadowland in summer, and of kale in winter.

One of our greatest losses in good grassland has been due to the disappearance of sheep-walks on the chalk downs. By the loss of sheep, coupled with military occupation and over-cropping with corn, large areas have degenerated into rough grazings, and the close, springy turf has become a disgrace of thistle and ragwort. The return of the downland flocks, hurdled for barley or root-crops, is long overdue. Speaking of animal foods, we may mention in passing experiments in new ones: notably, hybrid maize in America, by means of which 700 million more bushels of maize have been produced in the U.S.A.; and, on poor land, *Lupinus mutabilis*, a lupin bred in the Andes, whose alkaline poison is washed out in the mountain streams to make it fit, with its 40% protein content, for human as well as animal consumption. Russian Comfrey is yet another valuable fodder novelty.

On sticky valley bottoms of "four-horse" heavy land, draining and liming (ground-limestone is far superior to burnt lime) are indispensable. For lighter lands, the old custom of "marling"

[1] *op cit.*, p. 438.

might to advantage be restored; on sour and intractable soils, discing-in organic materials (what the Americans call "trash-farming") and subsoiling to prevent "hard pan" (an impervious layer of earth between topsoil and subsoil caused by tractor-ploughing at the wrong time or during a rainy period) are an adaptation or recovery of a good husbandry so often derided as "primitive". To give an example of the numbers of "unemployed" needed to carry out these and similar works, Stapledon's estimate per annum is 20,000 men for water-facilities to the fields, 50,000 for hedging and fencing, 2,000 for bracken in the Welsh hills, 15,000 for eliminating docks and 14,000 for dealing with rat and rabbit plagues.

Other methods of extending the acreage of land for cultivation or pasturing are by rescuing sea-drowned meadows, pumping shallow estuaries, coaxing mud-flats and sand-dunes into husbandry, and warping. The last is, or rather was (for it is almost disused), a most ingenious method practised in the Fens, Lincolnshire and the Isle of Axholme, of depositing silt on farmland by controlled flooding. Sea-swallowed land is ready for reclamation when the silt-banks are covered only by the highest tides. The salt can be washed out both by rain and drainage, and so the land is converted from salt to fresh beef-cattle marsh, and after pasturage to arable. Sand-dunes in their turn can be raised from poverty to wealth by sowing down with fescue grasses. Did not the great Coke of Norfolk resurrect the coastal barrens of his estate by much the same means?

*

These instances all stress the regional approach to the task of making the wilderness blossom, for each area of land to be redeemed is embedded in local conditions of soil, vegetation, temperature, rainfall and geographical site. How greatly, for instance, would it benefit the growing of fruit and vegetables (for the latter Dr. Stamp proposes 150% increase) if distribution were decentralized from Covent Garden; also, if both were in part linked with the economy of the individual farm, taking their place in its rotations, just as in France the walnut tree stands in the fields and as in both France and Kent the orchards are kept in good heart by mixed grazing. In the same way, the over-specialized market-garden should have some relation to the farm. Dr. Stamp's figures for the potential increase of market-gardening are from 1,100,000 acres to 2,820,000, and production on such a scale is open to abuse on many counts unless vegetable- and fruit-growing are more closely interwoven with farm-crops than they are now.

Inseparably allied to such regionalism in curing the land of its present sickness is the local consumption of the produce it is to bear. The saving in transport alone would run into astronomical figures, and the regional householder's ignorance of where his food comes from and how it is grown would no longer be total. But by far the most important result would be an inestimable gain in the standard of nutrition. Modern masses are never more than half-fed and the preservatives, the bleaching, the colouring, the flavouring, the "improving", the processing and the adulteration of foods carried over vast distances[1] is one of the major vices of our age, an even more virulent industrial ramp than profiteering on their transport and distribution. Malnutrition is indeed creating a nation of invalids, for in all this doctoring of foodstuffs people have not shrunk from the use of such toxic chemicals as nitrogen trichloride (agene), dulcin, azo-dye and others. In the Middle Ages, the adulterator of food was tied to the ducking-stool and plunged into the local pond. Nowadays, he sits under showers of gold and honours.

Quality in diet is very closely related to land-use. It is plain, for instance, that local consumption means bringing the people to their food, and not, as now, bringing their food to the people; and this implies a re-settlement of the land on a regional basis. "Nutritionists", again, are agreed as to the incomparable superiority of fresh over prepared foods, a condition best fulfilled by the natural and dairy foods, fruit, vegetables, eggs,

[1] See Chapter VII, for a further discussion on food-adulteration.

butter and cheese. Where else but from the resources of our own land are we in the future to obtain butter and cheese? The increased turnover would profoundly modify and fertilize existing land-use by, as we have already said, the return of the by-products both for stock-feeding and enriching the land.

But ecological interdependence does not stop there. The return of butter- and cheese-making to the farms would give just the right opportunity for multiplying our pig-population from 2 to 16 million, as discussed in Chapter IV and as recommended in the "Progress Report". The pig is one of the most economical of animals for converting wastes both in land and food into protein, while skim milk and whey are ideal foods for young porkers and baconers. Chat (small) potatoes, rye and maize, fodder-beet and barley are other unexacting pig-foods, while a good sow should produce twenty pigs a year. Hence, as we shall continue to stress, pigs are a vital link in the chain between grass, cow, milk and cheese or butter, not to mention their rich manurial value for the fertility of the land.

But quality in food has a direct influence not only upon the quality of land but upon quantity in land-surface. If, for instance, the staple of life were not robbed of the wheat-germ from the national loaf to increase the profits of the millers, but left in the grain of wheat where nature put it, the whole-grain loaf would enable us to increase the food-value of our wheat acreage by 20%, at the same time trebling or quadrupling the nutritional value of every loaf. More, since whole-grain flour, whether white (by lessening the bran content) or brown, can only be ground by the stone-grinding and not by the industrialized roller mill, the re-conditioning of our windmills and watermills, of which a few only survive as picturesque ruins is highly desirable. Such mills, if only as auxiliaries, and with the aid of turbines, would automatically regulate the current of our rivers, sweeten the waters and check the growth of weeds and rushes. For we can no more afford to waste power, than food. The disingenuous excuse made by the millers that the extraction of the wheat-germ means more feeding-stuffs for beasts is easily put aside for the evasion it is, when we consider how enormously we could increase lucerne as a crop in this country and ensilage for winter fodder, not to mention sugar-beet tops.

The more we intensify, by the avoidance of monoculture and the extension of mixed farming, the productive powers of the farm acreage already in cultivation, the less onerous becomes the task of reclaiming wasteland and restoring built-over land to its proper purpose. Heaven knows there will be enough to do for those missing, forsaken, urbanized, deadened and violated acres described in Chapter III, even were we to elevate the whole of our cultivated acreage to the high standard of the English garden. But this standard would at least leave us with a margin; we should not be attempting the impossible. Some of the built-over land cannot be re-converted without almost superhuman effort. But then, what are machines for, if not to make us superhuman? The question remains—how much of it can we afford to leave alone without being half-hearted in approaching our goal of self-sufficiency? And how much more open land can we afford to hand over for non-agricultural use in the future? The answer should work itself out as we go ahead in our creative endeavour, and a new Domesday Book, as suggested by Sir George Stapledon, would be of invaluable service to that end.

Take housing. Dr. Stamp's calculation is that, averaging ten houses to the acre, from 250,000 to 350,000 acres will be required to carry out the new housing schemes. It is obvious that planting new houses on good farming land *must be stopped for good and all*. But that is not enough. Dr. Stamp has proposed new housing on abandoned but regenerated industrial sites—he mentions, for instance, 9,000 acres in the Black Country. We may add that the abandoning of such existing sites is bound to spread as the export trade peters out. Another idea is to pile up the houses vertically instead of extending them horizontally. Only a generation which has lost confidence in itself is afraid of such innovations. Much might be done in reconditioning old cottages according to the very economical formula set out by W. H. Godfrey in *Our Building Inheritance*,[1] instead of condemning them out of hand as the county councils do. Again, where gardens are attached to new houses, it should be obligatory on the tenant to cultivate them intensively, a measure which would by no means be an edict of banishment for flowers and lawns which contribute to the productiveness of the garden by way of the compost stack. A happier prospect is the multiplication of cottage homesteads as our void countryside becomes re-peopled by a new peasantry.

As for the sprawl of factories over our once-smiling countryside, many of these will be put out of use as industry contracts instead of expanding, and its demands on space become less. For a twentieth-century industry, however prosperous, need not sprawl, and if an individual factory should need more room, then let it grow upwards, not outwards. We must let the procreative blessings of air, light and fertility into the smothered land on which the factory-slums stand. Forestry, the marginal lands and the water-supply we have already reviewed, however inadequately from lack of space. As to the last, we need hardly add that the trapping of rain-water by an inter-linked system of storage tanks should be universal, while the extravagant town-consumption of water may even then have to be curtailed. The re-settlement of the land by *men*, the most vital of all the great works that lie ahead, is the subject of the next chapters.

As for parks and recreation grounds, are they any the less recreative, less desirable, less satisfying if they grow good crops and feed good beasts as well? Or if we add herb-gardens, vineyards and orchards to them? The old craftsmen whom our civilization liquidated could have reminded us of the gracious interplay between use and beauty. Orchards, of course, border many of the French roads, but in this country, they say, the fruit would be stolen. Our answer to this is that a nation of

[1] Faber, 1944.

thieves does not deserve to become self-supporting or indeed to survive at all. Passing on to the monster concrete stadia for dog- and motor-racing, we are reminded of the old Spanish proverb—"Take what you will, said God; take it, but pay for it!" They are modern versions of the Roman amphitheatre, pandering to the passions of a dispossessed proletariat which, like ours, was once rooted to the soil. Horse-racing studs and stables could certainly be reduced without hardship too heavy to be borne, while golf-links could be confined to the most sterile types of land and the majority of roads linked to the land by a more regional distribution of them. As for the Fat Boy cities, they will slim themselves as industrialism inevitably yields precedence to agriculture, and becomes really efficient; and as the countryside fills up. Whatever the pangs of transition, it is hardly a tragedy of the first order that urbanism should be transformed into urbanity.

All these measures, or most of them, will be carried out if the finger of necessity touches the heart and soul of Great Britain. What has been set out in so prosaic a fashion will on the contrary appear to many as a Utopian vision, and we are rightly tired of Utopian dreamers. But that the present industrial structure can be preserved intact, and that the ingenuity of the technocrat is able by his charms to call up a magic ship for carrying us over a sea of troubles—this is a fantasy wilder than any Wonderland.

In the history of every nation there comes a time when it has to choose its future destiny or perish of its own stupidity and inertia. It should be plain by now that, having erred from the path of wisdom, we are in danger of being lost for ever. But the alternative still remains—namely, "Tomorrow to fresh woods, and pastures new".

H. J. Massingham

CHAPTER VI

The Return of the Peasant

IN PREVIOUS chapters we have been forced by the facts to the conclusion that our industrial civilization does not know how to look after its own country and certainly does not know how to farm it. This is a very simple proposition that is entirely unacceptable to government, industry and science. But the conditions prevailing both on the farms, in the countryside, and in the food markets prove it to be true, and mere opinion on the other side cannot make a ha'porth of difference to its validity. The spread of plant disease and the multiplication of pests despite all the ingenious measures taken, not to prevent but to cure; falling soil fertility; the wounds and sores and ulcers of open-cast mining, gravel-digging and the like, festering the body of the maternal earth; the swallowing up of more and more land for any purpose other than agriculture; the expansion of wasteland like ink on blotting-paper—are witnesses against which there is no convincing appeal.

If the meaning of all this is not heeded, it is because our age either does not wish, or is too blinded to heed it. The blind lead the blind into the ditch, and this particular ditch is bottomless. Our one chance of survival is to call a halt, for we are already on the brink.

Actually, the overall remedy is as simple as the proposition itself, thorny and complicated as are the means thereto because there is so much more to unlearn than to learn. If the nation as a whole has forgotten how to look after its own country and how to farm it, what is needed is to put it in charge of those who know how to cultivate it. And the only men who can and will do so are clearly those most attached to the land, both as belonging to it and being responsible for it. This is an entirely different thing from making a business of it ("the agricultural industry"); it is making a good thing of it, not a good thing *out* of it. In Western Europe today there is generally speaking only one type of cultivator who properly fulfils these functions, though of course other types exist in smaller numbers. This is the peasant. Therefore, there is no alternative open to us, on the brink of the pit of famine as we are, except to re-create a peasantry.

*

If any reader is disposed to question whether what is written in the first paragraph is not sensational rather than true, let him discover for himself the all-but-universal view of the peasant held by modern society and particularly by its men of science. The peasant in our country today is the most despised and rejected among men. Not the meanest of bottle-washers holds a lower place in public and learned estimation. He is outside the pale, a kind of uncouth Caliban. Tramps and gipsies have their haloes, but the name of the peasant is mud. He is "the primitive", much in the sense that the fastidious Houhyhnms in *Gulliver's Travels* regarded the Yahoos. He is a picturesque bygone, a romantic anachronism, a hangover from the dark ages, but he is also the loutish drudge who fecklessly toils and moils from morning to night without a thought in his dull brain of achieving a "standard of living". Of all the motley stragglers out of the past who have drifted into the present he is the most "uneconomic"; nor can the machine of a progressive agriculture work "efficiently" until this piece of grit in it is removed.[1]

Note two of the more prominent spot lights that glare down upon this unfortunate obstruction to a rationalized agriculture. They are not man-in-the-street prejudices; on the contrary,

[1] See, for instance, the book, *Four Thousand Million Mouths* (Oxford Univ. Press, 1951), written by a bevy of English "scientific humanists", in which the peasant appears over and over again as the scapegoat for the agricultural evils of our time. One of them talks of the change-over from "*exhaustive* subsistence farming to *conservative* commercial farming" (italics mine).

they proceed from the *élite* of the modern world, from scientific authority. Then again, the peasant is prosecuted on *historical* grounds; he is a misfit from the past. But if we, following this scientific lead, ourselves survey past civilizations in that impartial spirit of detachment which is presumed to be the scientific watchword, what do we discover? That in all ages and in all the quarters of the globe, the peasant has been to the general community exactly what its roots are to the plant. The very exceptions prove the rule. Those civilizations like the Roman, the Carthaginian, the Assyrian and other predatory slave-empires which either dispensed with a peasantry or dispossessed their original ones, withered and fell to pieces because they had never grown, or had cut, their own roots.

This is indisputable; it is one of the clearest and at the same time one of the deepest laws and verities of history. Here is not the place to enlarge upon the durability of peasant cultures; it has recently been presented in *Soil and Civilization*,[1] while a host of historians, including our contemporary, A. J. Toynbee, have shown it to be true. Against this *datum* of history, therefore, one as unquestionable as the rise and fall of empires themselves, the modern scientific special pleading against the peasant is seen in its true light. We need attach no more importance to it than to a schoolboy delivering historical judgments when all he knows is the dates of the Kings of England. "They [the Scottish peasants or crofters]", wrote Lewis Grassic Gibbon in his trilogy, *The Scots Quair*, "endure the chatter of the city salons, the planning of this and that war and blockade, they endure the pretensions of every social class but their own to be the mainspring and base of human society—they, the masters who feed the world!"

Let us leave for the moment the reason for such gross misjudgment by agricultural science. We have first to turn from past to present, from the historical to the contemporary peasant. It is an ironical point of modern history that our population, which has been taught by its science to look down upon the

[1] Edward Hyams (Thames and Hudson, 1951).

demoded peasant as a figure of dirt, drudgery and the dead end, has been very largely dependent upon him for its butter and bacon. Denmark, indeed, is a nation of peasants, as are all the Scandinavian countries: 96% of the Swedes, 98% of the Norwegians and 86% of the Danes are coöperative mixed farmers cultivating less than 75 acres per family. In Switzerland the percentage is 97. If we throw in France, which has always been a peasant nation, and substract for the moment other sources of imported food-supplies, such as the Argentine, the Dominions and the tropics, it can be said with justice that the man who has been keeping us alive in the more essential or "protective" foods during our century has been the West European peasant—and that, of course, thanks to our economic system, at the expense of our own pig-producers, who might have bred millions of pigs which take up very little room and at the same time enhance the farm's fertility. Turning up our noses at the peasant has not precluded us from opening our cuckoo mouths for the foster-bird from Europe to feed us. As King Lear remarked upon the ingratitude of his daughters,

> Is it not as this mouth should tear this hand
> For lifting food to 't?

In fact, so far from the Danes being a "backward" country run by "primitive" clodhoppers, Adamite diggers and delvers, they have, corrupted by our economics, gone almost too far in the other direction. That is to say, they became too prosperous as a highly organized small-scale farming community with coöperative marketing and fell victim to the money-system by deserting their own wise subsistence economy, exporting *more* than their surpluses and feeding their own people on inferior imports from the East. So rapidly did the Danes advance as a food-producing nation of peasants, with their coöperative societies, saving and credit institutions, group settlements for buying and selling, land-training camps and occupation centres, and their collaboration between trained mechanic and skilled husbandman, that they became too big for their boots. The temptation of easy money and the bargain-counter from Big Business Britain proved too much for them. In the circumstances, it hardly seems the last word in wisdom to play down the peasant as we do today, when a comparison between the yields of the West European peasant and those of the U.S.A. farmer shows that the former produces from 50 to 70 bushels per acre, the latter from 15 to 20.

It is, of course, true that not all peasant societies in Europe have reached anything like the brilliance of achievement the Scandinavian peasant has sought and won. On the contrary, the depression of the peasantries of Eastern Europe is common knowledge. But what else could possibly be expected when the attempted imposition upon them of a collective system runs against the very grain and bias of peasant status, peasant tradition, peasant independence and peasant control over the land of his roots, his sweat and his heart? It is no good looking for a fertile, well-husbanded, and so productive soil from a peasantry either exploited for purely commercial ends or victimized by the latest edition of the slave-making empire; nor where the peasant, as in Italy, is deprived of land to work, tools to work with and even a minimum of necessary capital.

*

We turn now to examples here and there of peasant holdings surviving in our own country; the pariahs, so to speak, of our farming lands. But before doing so, it is proper to say that the peasant is not without defenders even in Britain, even in the land of the landless labourer, even in "the agricultural industry" of the saurian machine, of cost-cutting, profit and loss accountancy, of the fertilizer bill, "efficiency", cash-cropping for export and the factory-farm. Sir George Stapledon should be mentioned with particular honour, for his minority voice has made itself heard out of the narrow corridor and dense atmosphere of orthodox specialism. "I think", he has said, "there is grave risk of the family farmer being slowly and steadily swallowed up by large and fully equipped farming companies, and this to my mind would be the greatest ill that could befall the countryside." Again, "I believe the movement in the direction of owner-occupiers will in the long run be the salvation of our agriculture", and "For a healthy and vigorous countryside there should be as many owner-occupiers as possible".

His championship of "the owner-occupier" may be placed side by side with the view of Professor R. H. Tawney[1] on the curse of functionless property:

> There is no inconsistency between encouraging simultaneously a multiplication of peasant farmers and small masters to own their own farms and shops and the abolition of private ownership in those industries in which the private owner is an absentee shareholder.

Professor A. J. Toynbee, in his turn, has demonstrated, in *A Study of History*, the calamities that fall upon States which interfere with, oppress, exploit, cheat or abolish their peasant foundations. Professor Boutfleur, a pontiff of modernized agriculture, adds his supplementary word: "History has told us that no form of big farming, mechanized or otherwise, can compete against a peasantry." And Lord Ernle, once Minister of Agriculture, who may be called the official historian of our native agriculture, crowns this anthology with:

> If the attractions of towns are to be counteracted and agricultural labourers lifted from apathy and hopelessness to contentment and activity, a purpose must be given to village life. Probably this can be done effectively by giving labourers ready access to land and access as owners. Tenancies may to a certain extent produce similar results. . . . But the incentive of ownership is incomparably the stronger. . . . It is only by ownership that the atmosphere can be recreated in which the peasant becomes part of the land and the land part of him.[2]

The fact that these dissentient voices from orthodox opinion are deliberately chosen from an orthodox medium lends the

[1] *The Acquisitive Society*. [2] But see Chapter VII.

greater weight to their words. Sanity may speak with a still, small voice, but it is heard in the end above all the winds of clamour.

We have room here to give only four examples of peasant farming in Britain at the present day, two of them communities, one large and well-known and the other small and obscure, two of them individual farmers, one well known from his books, the other known only to ourselves and a few others. The crofters of Scotland and the Isles, who are true peasants, must be left out because, like those of Eastern Europe, their condition and status have been artificially depressed by vicious economic forces from without, against which they have been helpless. The learned and unlearned who scorn the peasant and want to be rid of him always speak of him as a piece of antiquity clogging the wheels of the proletarian present. No prejudice could be worse-founded. The only valid test of a peasant in his relation to the soil is whether he is a true or a sham peasant; if he be a true one, "bred in the bone, past and present become merged"—to quote Neville Cardus in a cricketing context. Whether he uses a Ferguson tractor or two pair of oxen is quite irrelevant, although it is a fact that a very large number of the European peasants who have been feeding our superior selves—feeding the cuckoo—use primitive implements. What counts is something quite different—by now we have a glimmering of what it is.

The largest community of peasants in England is the Vale of Evesham group, and 80% of its holdings are under 15 acres per family. Both in origin and characteristics it is decidedly a peasant society. The earliest occupants were chiefly members of Joseph Arch's Union of Agricultural Labourers, who were ex-peasants charged off their land by the Enclosures. Before the Evesham Council took over, the landlords were forced by the Great Depression of the 'seventies of last century to let out holdings on land reverted to waste, and since the main object of Joseph Arch himself was to reinstate the peasantry, these ex-peasants became ex-labourers. Under the Evesham Custom these new landed little men obtained their holdings on very favourable terms, endorsed by the Council in security of tenure, benefit from improvements and independence of action. The gap in continuity was bridged over.

In many aspects of their lives as small producers, the family-farmers of the Vale ran true to peasant type. The drift from the land was stopped and the current actually began to flow the other way. The families fed themselves off their own land and home-made their own bread and bacon; the wives shared their husbands' land-work and picked and tied the fruit and vegetables for market; a vigorous communal life was centred round the village hall; the range of occupation was wide and varied; there was no social gap between master and workman and, most important of all, the ladder of apprenticeship between landless and landed was not overturned. What is even more suggestive, the strip system of the medieval open field village community was maintained in the sense that 395 occupiers held 850 different "cuts" of land in different areas, not out of an inert conservatism, but simply because these separate plots were best suited for certain crops. A pattern of crops was established, so that the holders avoided putting all their eggs into one basket. The Littleton and Badsey Growers, Ltd. (1908) organized the marketing, raising the turnover from £4,283 in 1909 to £359,800 in 1945. During the slump periods of depression, a normal feature of modern agriculture, these small producers saved themselves from the wreckage of their markets by reverting to the old canon of self-subsistence, retiring snail-wise into their shells. This is highly significant.

And there's the rub! The corruption of the best is the worst, as the old Latin proverb says. There was a flaw in the structure of this façade, hidden under the brightness of its paint. The pressure of the modern world was too exacting; the temptation to conform to it, too strong. And you have only to read the Astor-Rowntree Report on British Agriculture and the writings of the late Sir Daniel Hall, to note how weighty was the battering-ram brought against the walls of the authentic peasant values. At any rate, the small growers of the Vale were seduced and compelled by the logic of their own success-story to desert those values and to become something like an export corporation on a large scale. In other words, they have overdone their cash-cropping; the fertility of their holdings has steadily declined in consequence; the loss of humus has been so severe that they have had to rely almost solely on large importations of artificial fertilizers, and soil-exhaustion is round the corner. As in most modern farming, quality was sacrificed to quantity and money-valuations got the whip-hand of good husbandry. For, with the genuine peasant, fertility takes precedence of production and the export of surpluses only inhibits wholesale cash-cropping.

The smaller community to which we have referred resembles the much larger one of the Vale of Evesham, in that land (450 acres) is rented with security of tenure from a County Council (Norfolk) and that its occupiers were also landless labourers and the sons of farmers whose thrift had enabled them to lay by a little money. But it differs in the division of this acreage, on the principle of the mixed farm, into seven 50-acre holdings, five 7-acre holdings and four whose sizes range from 10 to 15 acres, all of them rented very low. There has, therefore, been no inducement for a tenant to extend his holding at the expense of an intensive husbandry. Within these wise limits a traditional peasant economy has taken root and flourishes, regardless of those palliatives, such as shorter hours, higher wages, access to urban delights, and so on, which divert the landless labourer's attention from the fundamental loss he suffers in being no longer master of the land he cultivates.

One of the present authors[1] was so fortunate as to be able to publish an account of this little peasant estate which had been recorded by a man who with the aid of his wife has himself worked one of the 7-acre holdings for several years. But, being a professional writer as well, this man is sufficiently detached from the community to take conscious measure of it. The

[1] H. J. Massingham.

tenants all practise the four-course Norfolk rotation of crops, largely disused among the larger farms of the neighbourhood. The estate is amply stocked with fattening bullocks on the marshy areas and pigs in yards for muck-making, with poultry folded over ley and stubble and sheep on the lighter lands, geese and goats in the orchards and even horses, while the variety of crops grown on these tiny farms is extraordinary.

On one of them, for instance, currants, strawberries, raspberry canes, barley, sugar-beet, hay, mangolds, potatoes, market vegetables and wheat in strips are grown on 3½ acres, so that the land is kept continuously on the move. Cash-expenditure amounts to little more than 10*s*. a week, and every possible penny is put back into the family holding. These miniature farms are rich, not in a bank but in a fertility balance, four of the 7-acre holdings fattening eighteen bullocks a year and producing 90 tons of muck for the 28 acres. The horses are mainly used for winter-ploughing when the tractor is helpless, as is rarely done on the bigger farms of the region, which have no horses. Wholeness of husbandry of this kind has, in consequence, produced such yields as none of the commercial farms can compete with. A good farmer's sugar-beet yield is 10 tons per acre; these holdings produce from 13 to 14, one ½-acre piece yielding 19 tons.

Self-help at this, its highest, pitch is interwoven with neighbourly help, as among French peasants, so that the community as a whole has developed "an intensely parochial social outlook". The families intermarry and three surnames go to nine of the holdings. The writer describes the cultivations as intensive and unspecialized, carried out by what he calls "beautiful timing and planning", a devoted attention to detail and close observation of changes in weather, season and soil-texture, acted upon precisely as the occasion demands. The very smallness of this cluster of farms has entailed a highly complex integration in their husbandry, while the land itself is kept "clean as wax".

The interdependence between crop and stock, field and field

is reflected in the lives of the community itself, whose members organize their own cricket team, collect wild fruits in the lanes, visit one another and, most important of all, bring up their children in intimate contact with the soil of their fathers' labours and their mothers' homesteading. It is evident from the example of this minute settlement how great are the potentialities of a true homestead economy of peasants in enriching the fertility of the land, multiplying its production of crop and stock and affording the cultivator a stable, skilled and responsible livelihood. "I cannot think", the description ends, "but that the whole enterprise has been one of 'great pith and moment'; and if, through lack of the necessary recognition and encouragement, its current should turn awry, it would be yet another symptom of the complete decadence of our national policy." Contrast the rich orderliness of this group with the beggarly mess and muddle that nationally prevails outside it. And what encouragement does that policy grant the land-hungry applicant for a holding when one County Council in Lincolnshire has a waiting list of 800 such applicants, while in Scotland alone there is a waiting list of 10,000?

As an example of the individual peasant at work, we choose a Welsh sheep-farmer of the Cader Idris region with whom one of us stayed for some time in his sturdy farmstead of grim "slatestone" on the mountainside. Perhaps he should be called yeoman rather than peasant, but the yeoman is only a peasant magnified. Both, where not unbalanced by the pressure of finance, specialism or economic theory, practise the bedrock principles of husbandry, neither as proletarian nor capitalist, since their fundamental concern is neither with wages nor profit but with the real wealth of the land. It is because of this primary attachment between man and soil, "the stake in the land", that the degradation of the peasant (as in India, for instance) is always in the long run followed by the degradation of the land.

This farmer, who owns 240 acres, of which 200 are sheep-walk and the rest arable and hay, revealed that true farming revolves on its own axis as a sphere, and that to turn it into a straight line of export in the manner of orthodox commercial farming is a polite term for brigandage and anarchy. The centre of the sphere was himself and the spokes all radiated to the circumference. He even made his own quill-pens from the primary feathers of his geese! His two sons and a German prisoner were extensions, like tools, of his own hands, and his farm was stocked as full as it would hold with Welsh Black cattle, pigs, poultry, ponies for the mountain gathering of the sheep, and 300 sheep. He had his finger in every pie. He was at once flockmaster, shepherd, herdsman, ploughman, haymaker, dog-trainer, builder, vet. and meteorologist, and his only cash transactions were the sale of wool and mutton. The only machine was a straw-baler and the hay was cocked and seasoned by the admirable tripod system. Most of the arable land in rape, ley-mixtures, oats, potatoes and dredge corn was for the stock, so that all the parts of the farm economy were interlocked into a single organic whole.

Nor did he confine his activities to his own farm. He was an official of the local Farmers' Union and took his personal part in the communal sheep-shearing gatherings of the small farmers that were so striking and beautiful a feature of the neighbourhood. They were a voluntary expression of mutual aid, based upon the family, in that women, children and men all took part in the several functions, unpaid, which were held in barns, in the *ffridds* or open enclosures, or on the bare mountain plateau. We used to go with him to these exhilarating meetings, so timeless and immemorial that one might have stepped into the Old Testament or the novels of Thomas Hardy or Shakespeare's *The Winter's Tale*. We could see from such experiences how naturally coöperative the peasant is when not persecuted nor forced into the mould of an alien money-system; and how readily the religious festival might have sprung from such common and neighbourly needs. Nor were all these activities the end of this yeoman-peasant's plenitude of living, for he was a reader and a thinker as well, a man both of historical and an altogether exceptional topographical knowledge. He was the exact counterpart of the man who, in the Scriptures, went after the hundredth sheep.

We must spare, too, a little room for one last example of our native peasants in action; very briefly, because this man has told his own story in a couple of books. George Henderson, who began his farming career as a shepherd in Scotland, farms 85 acres of thin or "brashy" land a few inches over rock in the eastern Cotswolds. When we first visited this farm, it disclosed its whereabouts simply by the quality of the crops, instantaneously recognizable beyond all others we had seen in fifty miles of travel. No wonder, for it was as heavily stocked with cattle, sheep, pigs, poultry, geese, ducks and horses as a farm could hold.

The agricultural returns showed that he carried thrice as much cattle, four times as many sheep, ten times as many pigs and twenty-five times as much poultry as did the average of all other farms in the county, while he and his brother each worked 80 hours a week and spent 600 hours a year spreading muck. In a few years and by means of the utmost variety of interdependent cropping and stocking, the Henderson brothers raised the value of their farm from £7 an acre to £150, of the Jersey herd from £50 to £3,000, and the grain yields from 7 to 20 quarters per acre. This massive transformation was accomplished not by wage-labour, but that of student apprentices. Henderson is a very different type from our modest and retiring master-man of the Welsh Mountains and yet both are essentially peasants in their full cultivation of the land, the austerity of hard work, the pursuit of an intensive mixed husbandry, the export of surpluses only, their allegiance to the law of returning to the land what is taken from it, their sense of the soil as a vocation and of the farm as a unified economic organism of interacting parts.

"Enslavement to drudgery" is the verdict of the orthodox. But the sweat of stall and furrow did not prevent Henderson from writing two books about it.

*

It would appear, therefore, that the case against the peasant lacks even the shadow of a leg to stand on. *By the criterion of output per acre every other type of farmer is an "also ran"*. In the ignominious failure of a system of economics that has carried the nation within sight of the Polar ice-cap of famine and has reduced it to the pitiable subservience of scrambling for dollars, like a dog for a bone from the table of transatlantic Dives, it becomes obvious that of all men the peasant is the man we need to give sinew, heart and reality to the farming world. The stone that the builders rejected has to become the key-stone of the arch. To restore foundations we have to build on *him*. "Security" has become the nostrum of the most insecure of all our historical civilizations, so that the stability and continuity of a peasant economy answers its most vital need. It is through him, too, that we can win back our self-respect, for we have become a nation living on doles instead of finding our markets in the fruitful labours of our own land and its faithful cultivators. We have to build on the peasant because we are reduced to sheer economic impotence without him.

So we return to the question put in the early part of this chapter. If the attack on the peasant made by the grave and reverend signors of agricultural science is so feather-flimsy, what is the reason for it? The answer must be clear by now: because what the peasant represents is something entirely different from, the positive reverse of, what his detractors, who have behind them our whole economic and financial system, represent. We may illustrate the incompatibility between them by a quotation from a paper, *The Homestead Economy*, written by Mr. F. J. Jenks:

> A good housewife undoubtedly practises the art of household management; she is a real economist. But the professional economist . . . would find her uneconomic. For she works more hours a week than a Trades Union would allow and yet her "output" is negligible, there being no known mathematical means of measuring comfort, health and happiness. Indeed, he might very well bring forward a neat calculation to "prove"

that the replacement of a thousand housewives by a staff of 200 females operating a communal restaurant, dormitory, nursery and laundry, would not only effect a substantial cash saving but would "release" 800 units of labour for making goods for export.

Consider for a moment the principal needs of a peasant economy in order that it might become firmly re-established in this country. They are: stabilized prices; access to capital and credit facilities free of interest; an intensive mixed husbandry requiring abundance instead of scarcity of labour; an integrated economy of subsistence farming whereby home, family and labour interact; fullness of production based on the fertility of the soil and the sale of surpluses, and not on cash-cropping for export; variety and balance of crop and stock; manual work aided by small machines and not total mechanization supplemented by exiguous man-power; regional and co-operative buying and selling; the ladder of apprenticeship between pupil and master, son and father, farmer and labourer; work as a vocation and not as a penance to be mitigated by shorter hours and higher wages; small workshops and machine-shops attached to each community; a central control-farm to each settlement; the pooling of resources for larger undertakings; part-time workers producing food on their own plots for their families between day-labouring on other farms; decentralization, status and the revival of the tradition of mutual aid.

These prerequisites for a flourishing peasant agriculture have only to be listed, to reveal at a glance their radical incompatibility with factory-farming, its methods of specialization and its solely commercial incentive. Here lies the final explanation of why the very name of peasant is anathema to the kind of officers who now steer the ship of state and are driving it headlong upon the reef of famine. Yet no less than 78% (340,000) of existing holdings in this country are of less than 100 acres, the majority averaging between 5 and 50. It has been calculated that there are more than 3 million small producers at work in Britain, pseudo-peasants most of them, not real peasants, because they are depressed and hampered at every turn by the combination of an all-powerful system of economics with a mental climate hostile to them in grain. And how our governers think may be illustrated without comment by a statement in the Astor-Rowntree Report on British Agriculture issued during the second World War: "After this war there is likely to be too much food."

It has been well said that it is the modern concept of economic efficiency which alone keeps the land and the people apart.

We thus arrive at the conclusion that the rapid decline in our own time of the capitalist-industrialist system can and ought to accompany a corresponding release and elevation of the peasant economy and the peasant values. Now or never is the golden chance for reconstruction in the latter, to fill the vacuum caused by the failure of the former. It is preposterous to imagine that large-scale specialized business farms, equipped with monster machines and a few expensive hands working half the day in extracting the wealth of the soil and burning the straw (as I have seen done all over Wiltshire) can possibly, even by means of the neatest of account sheets, perform the titanic job of saving our over-populated nation from starvation. Over-populated in the cities, depopulated on the land. At a time when even official quarters have become aware of our dwindling food-supplies, our total farm income fell from £309,000,000, in 1949 to £264,500,000 in 1950-1. Labour scarcity is the principal cause of this alarming drop, and what answer can there be but to settle the landless on the land?

There is no escape from the bleakness of the prospect before us except by boldly choosing to turn sham into real peasants and to multiply the latter by a host of new ones. *An economy that husbands natural wealth is the proper antithesis of an "economics" that dissipates it.* And we should be the more heartened to this end by the fact that healthy peasant cultivation is sound ecological doctrine. It is the industrialist, not the farmer-craftsman, who breaks the rules of ecology. The peasant way is not that of a mathematical problem, nor is it a mere mechanism of production. His is the animate and biological approach, which establishes an intimate association between man and soil by means of a shorthand and concentrated application of nature's own methods of blending and balancing over the whole land-surface. For the due utilization of his own land the peasant, in part intuitively and in part by personal observation and attention, re-interprets what takes place in the general economy of nature. He practises the law of return, he interchanges crop and stock, he conserves soil-wealth and maintains the health of his living charges by noticing and adapting how nature works as an organism of multiple parts whose whole is something more than the sum of them. In his husbandry he links a natural with a human economy. He intensifies natural processes and modifies them, but always, if he be a genuine peasant, within ecological bounds. He gives in compensation for what he takes. Peasant cultivation necessarily implies a certain harmony with nature, as against the agricultural scientist's "conquest of nature" and the industrialist's slogan of "the world mine oyster". The very term "good husbandry" presupposes an ethic, a value, a quality, a responsibility with which the confusion between farms and firms can have nothing to do. Perhaps that is why a peasant society is rarely other than a religious one.

*

When he composed his famous epigram, "The magic of property turns sand into gold", Arthur Young, that champion of enclosure, contradicted his own policy which resulted in the loss of our traditional peasantry. That is the surest way of turning "economic units" into master-men; but it need not be the only way. Security of tenure at a low rental is another, and the county councils could play an important part as intermediaries between the landless labourer and the landed peasant, so that those shameful waiting-lists might become a healed sore of the unregenerate past. Large areas of land saved from exploitation or reclaimed from neglect by the State should be re-allotted to the land-worthy, subject only to inspection by the District Land Warden, and those conditions outlined in the next chapter.

It is not to be questioned that, since one-sixth of our farms occupy no less than a half of our agricultural land, there is room enough for peasant occupation. Not that we ourselves would look with anything but disquiet upon a policy of relentlessly dispossessing large farmers on a purely quantitative basis. That would merely be to swing to the opposite extreme. But it is very certain that we cannot afford the waste of land and the expenditure of fertility entailed by large-scale farming as a commercial enterprise. And our own observations tell us that a number of these *latifundia*, as the Romans called them, could ill stand up to competent scrutiny by a conscientious Land Warden. The more "efficient" they are, the more conspicuous is the absence of individual caretaking, the more likely the wastage of sections and corners of land, the more dubious the maintenance of the underlying fertility. A splitting or contraction, or both, of their acreage would certainly benefit the cultivation of these expansive farms; and peasant cultivation of their perimeters would improve the quality and density of the yields.

Nor can a nation with little enough margin between it and want afford to indulge in the exhibitionism of large-scale factory-farming, where the land is a kind of parade-ground for a complicated motor-show and the farm both de-natured and de-humanized.

Not that all our *latifundia* are engaged in land-brigandage—Lord Iveagh's huge estate in the Suffolk Breckland is a notable exception. The Hosier group of farms is another. Furthermore, we imagine that some of our larger farmers would be more than willing, if they only had the chance, to subordinate cash-cropping to a subsistence economy and the export of surpluses.

Nevertheless, it can never be overstressed that the difference between factory-farming and peasant-farming is the difference between a technology and a culture, and this is fundamental. By the test of ecology, it is the former, not the latter, which is vulnerable. If we are not to overstrain our natural resources in the act of becoming self-supporting, and so reduce ourselves to beggary in them, we have to put our trust first and foremost in the type of cultivator who puts fertility, which is natural wealth, before production, which means the spending of that wealth. The peasant *is* of this type. If he fails to be, it is because he is not living up to his name by obeying the natural law of return; or is not allowed to do so. The large farmer, in his turn, may not live up to the orthodox test of efficiency which puts production before fertility, because good business in his case has not over-ridden good husbandry. But the exceptions will be among the larger rather than the smaller producers, for the obvious reason that to them agriculture is "the industry", and the business of an industry is to convert raw materials into saleable goods. There are two kinds of efficiency, one social, the other technical; the former puts the human and the animate before the mechanical and the inanimate. The peasant-farmer pursues not an industry but a way of life, in which personal responsibility counts for more than delivering the goods, so that cash-cropping for export forms only a part, not the whole of his endeavour. His approach to the land is direct; not, or much less, through the medium of the machine, the "hand", the profit and the loss, the bought and the sold.

The land is the peasant's home, not his office; hence, to provide goods farmsteads for a re-established peasantry will be our obligation to it for saving us from hunger. At present, it is "uneconomic" to build farmsteads out of the local materials lying at a man's future door. Our economy will be less subject to such absurdities when peasant settlements naturally proliferate into small workshops at their circumference, workshops for such essentials as building, tool-making, smithying, leather-working and what not. In the sheep-farming region of Wales to which we referred earlier in this chapter, for instance, there were a dozen small wool-factories and tanneries which, when we were staying there, had only recently become disused in the devouring interests of centralization. It is perfectly normal and healthy, not a perverse "backwardness", for a community of small producers to throw off side-shoots of these ancillary crafts and trades.

Such organic growths take time to develop, and in the meantime there is no reason at all against building homesteads in local material, whether earth and straw like Devon "cob" and Buckinghamshire "wichert", or Cotswold stone. Such buildings are comely in themselves, growing out of, rather than imposed upon the land (like ribbon development), durable for centuries, made of the substances least costly in transport and handling.

That it should be considered "cheaper" to transport machine-made bricks from Bedfordshire or Lincolnshire in order to build a house 500 miles away; or to dump pre-fabricated boxes, made equally far afield, in rows on the outskirts of villages and small towns, than to make use of the natural materials any given landscape supplies gratis, is only one more example of the abyss of unreality down which our economic system has pushed us. In a "real" world, we could save as much transport and manufacture by building houses out of the earth, as we could the expensive tackle of haysel and harvest by drying our corn and hay on tripods. This simple but proven device consists of a cone of three poles wired together at the top and near the bottom; the grass or corn is then draped over it in such a way as to give full play to the circulation of air. This is not "backward", but common-sense agriculture.

In a peasant community, a contractor service run by a co-operative group could readily carry out such heavy mechanical work as subsoiling, muck-shifting, ditching, threshing and the like for the individual holders. But the Great Machines of modern agriculture, like the Great Reptiles of the Jurassic Age, are so over-specialized that during the short time of the year when they are not idle they compel the farmer to do their will rather than his. He *must* become a specialist in order to use them. As they automatically clatter along an inevitable line of progressive development from the simple to the complex, so man himself is considered as a machine, automatically advancing from the small farmer to the large, from the husbandman to the mechanic, from subsistence to commercial agriculture and from coöperation with nature to conquest over nature. This fashionable concept sufficiently explains why modern man has swept over the earth like a prairie fire leaving behind him eroded soils, desert landscapes, de-forested hillsides and a wasteland that condemns him to an imminent world-starvation from which only the "backwardness" of the peasant can save him.

Throughout these chapters, we have seen that a double undertaking lies before the cultivator of the immediate future: on the physical plane he must save society from the immeasurable folly of its own economic system; on the spiritual plane, he must restore to man the creative functions he has lost. Ecology in the larger sense, and peasant-farming in the smaller, are both indispensable means to these ends, and that is why ecology is more than a science. It encompasses what the sciences of our day leave out. Peasant and ecologist recognize the underlying design of natural law, and re-arrange it into new combinations and permutations; for a house is more than four walls and a roof. But it would be futile in an age like our own, blinded by its illusions, to put forward such a proposition merely as argument. The fact is that our industrial civilization, which has destroyed values for valuations, is at the end of its tether. It has no future because it has sterilized itself. With the loss of the export market the whole system topples, first by living on capital, then by inflating the currency and lastly by bankruptcy. At present, the system survives only by expedients and evasions. But the time has come when our farms can no longer be sacrificed on the altar of industrialism. There is no escape but to cultivate our own garden, and the gardener in all ages is the peasant.

The peasant's potential use of the machine is, therefore, an issue of the greatest importance. Cash-cropping, monoculture, exploitation and exhaustion of the soil, depopulation of the land, and the big machines have in our own time all tended to go together. Not inevitably so, since in the man-made deserts of North Africa and the Middle East the big machine has played an impressively serviceable part in large-scale reclamation works. It is wrong-headed to indict the big machine simply because of its size and mechanical power; but, as we once heard a very shrewd and eminent farmer say, the machine is "permissive of evil", and under the pressure of an economic system that considers neither the land nor the farmer, it has had a bad and even sinister influence in de-populating the one and de-humanizing the other. Therefore, the development of the variable small machine to fit the variable nature of a peasant's mixed holding is the key to relieving one of the most formidable tragedies of our age—man's loss of humanity to a grossly mechanistic view of life.

Handy small machines like the rotary hoe, the planet junior for sowing seeds, the walking tractor and a score of others, possess the enormous advantage over the behemoths (as did the small mammals of the Eocene Age over the giant reptiles) in versatility, economical use of fuel, handiness, small storage-room, adaptability and other advantages of practical utility. Theirs is the serviceability of modesty, in the sense that they do not interfere with, still less shut off, man's intimate contact with the soil. They are flexible intermediaries, not specialized tyrants substituting mechanical valuations for human values. The "self-propelled tool-bar", for instance, is for row-crop cultivations no more than an extension of the hand-tool.

Nor is that heathen colossus, the giant power-station, the predestined means of generating electricity. With what utter disregard of a prudent economy do we waste the natural powers of wind, tide and current, and how easily could we set in motion our rotting tide-mills and watermills by means of manageable dynamos and turbines! What is it that makes our national bread a lie and a cheat? The big roller-mill that extracts the life-germ of the wheat-grain. What makes an honest loaf with all its vital elements intact? The small stone-grinding windmill, watermill or, even, the electric mill.

It would be both dangerous and superfluous to draw up a statistical blue-print with sections and sub-sections of particulars as to the methods and channels whereby a new peasantry can be established in our void and mutilated countryside, to codify the sizes of its farms, to draw up examination sheets of eligibility, to dictate cropping programmes, to prescribe hours of work and carry supervision to lengths paralysing individual initiative and freedom of action. A movement like this must come as an organic growth, be fostered in facilities and depend on improvisation. You cannot make a silk purse out of a sow's ear, but must build upon what goodness of material already exists. The Young Farmers' Clubs are already an admirable field of apprenticeship, and for the drastic changes in education that *are* imperative there is the guidance of the Scandinavian countries. The county council applicants reveal a submerged but powerful force looking, however subconsciously, towards a new orientation of society.

Here, as in other aspects of land-use, all occasions conspire and move towards a revaluation of the existing order (or disorder) as will put what is last first, and the first last. For survival demands, not that we shall make a new revolution in politics, government or institutions (was ever an age so plagued by revolutions as our century?), but that we shall change the ideas and preconceptions that gave birth to the Industrial Revolution and which are now driving it into a ruin which gives re-creation its chance. The position is really very simple. There is no way out for Britain but to become a self-supporting nation; a self-supporting nation must depend on its self-supporting farms, and the self-supporting farm is best maintained both in idea and practice by the peasant cultivator. If such logic generates the will to act upon it, the means thereto will not be lacking.

At present, our society is a purely urban one, consisting of a bureaucracy, specialists (by far the most dangerous members of the community), business managers and a proletariat of irresponsible machine-minders who have to be kept entertained, highly paid and employed at short hours in order to persuade them to endure the de-humanized conditions of their work. Yet even in this unpromising material a land-hunger representing a profound change towards a rural and responsible life makes itself felt not in statistics but in the very air we breathe. It is this new spirit, incoherent and tenuous as it seems to be, that alone can meet the demand of necessity that we shall change or die. As the seventeenth-century biographer, Thomas Fuller, wrote:

> It will not be amiss to pray that the plough may go along and the wheel around that, so being fed by the one and clothed by the other, there may be, by God's blessing, no danger of starvation in our nation.

CHAPTER VII

Modern Peasantry

In Chapter II we set out to show clearly our dependent situation in the matter of food, and in Chapter IV to sketch, very roughly and broadly, the potential of land available to us and of which we may make use, and must make use, if we are to become less dependent, and even independent. In Chapter VI we suggested that the best, if not the only, means of making this food-producing land viable, was by the restoration of a peasantry.

It is now necessary that we should explain more fully what is meant by this; but before doing so, it will be advisable to anticipate and meet some of the objections.

First of all, as we have already noticed, the very idea of a nation being self-supporting in food, turning back, as it were, to an old, rejected, parochial idea, and away from the modern "global" notion, the product of fast transport and of easy communications, is distasteful. Despite all that has happened to us, we are still, for the most part, Wellsians at heart. The editors of popular newspapers love to publish series of articles about vast schemes for reclaiming deserts and turning primeval forests into farmlands. Such articles are usually illustrated by photographs of scientists standing before, and dwarfed by, colossal wall-maps, with inset, perhaps, the air-helmeted profile of the Scientist-Hero, the new Hercules, the new Barbarossa, the new Myth-Hero. This is splendid, and it is to be hoped that political, economic and physical difficulties will not delay the consummation of the great plans by more than a century or so—a reasonable time for their realization. Meanwhile, we may feel hunger. Why not apply some science to our home problem? And some money? And some labour?

After all, even when the reclaimed Sahara is pouring millions of bushels of grain into the world markets, the depressed peoples of Africa and Asia will have first claim on this bounty: for it will be our own fault if their need is not greater than ours.

We apologize for the smallness and commonplace quality of the picture we are drawing. Unlike the magnificent plans mentioned above, our little scheme cannot flatter the sense of power and glory which editors like to tickle with their series of articles on draining the Mediterranean. All we offer is a square meal and quiet, congenial employment, plus, perhaps, a little surplus for art and science. And to justify this, our economic version of what might be called Little Englishry, we cannot help recalling the case of the pottery-seller, Alnashar. Alnashar sat in the market-stall where he sold his pots, day-dreaming of making his fortune; he had reached the point in his dream at which, the Sultan having begged him to marry his daughter, Alnashar spurned the love-sick Princess with his foot. So absorbed was the potter in his dream, that he really did kick out with his foot—and smashed all the pottery which was to be the foundation of his fortune.

We have also laid ourselves open to criticism by using the awful word "peasant"! This word will conjure up, in the minds of those hostile to our ideas, a mud-bespattered and illiterate boor, brutalized by toil and living in squalor; or, on the other hand, it will suggest a pretty, buxom girl in a fancy blouse, starched wimple and full-skirt dancing a morris. Our peasant, however, is a small farmer; he may own a television receiver and a car and a nice suit of clothes and some books; he may be a university graduate. He is a peasant because his farm will be run with two kinds of increase in mind: crops *and* fertility; subsistence *and* cash-crops.

We have now to describe the nature of the peasantry we propose to restore to Britain. With the means of doing this we shall deal in another chapter. As to the reason for doing it, we have already made that clear, but perhaps we may remind the reader of that reason in a brief summary: we need very large crops per acre; highly industrialized, very large farms worked by huge and specialized machines do not produce such crops; by the criterion of crops-per-acre they are very inefficient. We agree that such farms are very satisfying manifestations of man's power and glory, but most unfortunately we need to eat! In short, *we cannot afford the expensive luxury of "industrial" farming.*

OWNERSHIP AND SOCIALISM

Nothing emerges more clearly from a study of economic history than this fact: that the best can be got out of the land *only* by its owners. The land-owning peasant devotes himself not only to growing food and copious crops, to enrich himself, but to improving the soil, in order to leave a valuable property to his posterity. Everywhere in the world, including Britain, the best-farmed land is that of the owner-occupier-farmer, and whenever land has been taken away from the peasant, and the peasant reduced to the status of a tenant or labourer-for-hire, the land has suffered.

Yet property in land is a relatively modern idea, and when this idea was carried by Europeans to peoples less advanced in technics overseas, it was generally rejected with horror as a kind of blasphemy. With very rare exceptions, agricultural and pastoral cultures and civilizations have been founded, and have risen, on the axiom that the land belongs to everyone in common.

To reconcile this apparently fundamental feeling and idea with the undeniable fact that land is only well husbanded by its "owner", a number of interesting and ingenious compromises have in the past been devised. In all of them, however, the principle was the same. The land remained the property of the people, in the person of the Monarch, or the State, or the Republic. But the peasant became the owner *de facto*, the trustee *de jure*. He occupied the land, cultivated it as he saw fit or according to the custom of his community, as in the feudal system, or to the advice of agricultural scientists, as in the Incarial system. He owned the crop, disposed of it through his community, or by private dealing, and kept the proceeds, paying taxes, of course, like any other citizen. Moreover, his land passed to his son or sons, or sons and daughters.

In what sense, then, was such a peasant *not* a land-owner? In our, modern sense, he was certainly not a land-owner. For he could not alienate the land he occupied and cultivated; he could not sell it, give it away, use it for any purpose other than husbandry, leave it by will to a friend. In the last analysis, it was not his to dispose of; he held it in trust for the "people". He had all the advantages of ownership—freedom of farming, security of tenure, continuity of purpose and responsibility because his sons would inherit. But he was not free to commit the *crimes* of ownership—selling land to speculative builders, for example.

Nor, in the most successful ancient agrarian communities, was the land-holding peasant free to neglect or abuse the people's land. In the land-holding village communes of India, for example, the bad farmer could be dispossessed of his holding. In Peru, the peasant who wasted or made bad use of the water of irrigation supplied free by the State, was liable to be flogged. In the ancient Roman and Latin republics, the land-holder was not free to build his house on fertile land: he had to use bare rock or poor soil. Only in those highly advanced and corrupt societies which were powerful enough to extort food supplies from alien or colonial sources was the farmer at home free to make uneconomic use of soil, to abuse it, to neglect its fertility: that was because military force and financial seduction had replaced husbandry as the means of feeding the people and accumulating wealth.

If these things be true—and we believe that they are true and that a study of history confirms this belief, in every age and in every land—then it seems we are in a difficulty. To get the best out of our soil we must make the farmer the land-owner; but the whole movement of our times is, for excellent reasons, away from the idea of private ownership of the means of production, and towards public ownership. On grounds of justice, of equity, of social health, of economic efficiency, and for very powerful social-psychological reasons, this movement towards socialism is, despite temporary and local setbacks, the main tide of our time, and to attempt denying it or reversing it would be stupid and futile.

But perhaps the difficulty is not as great as it seems. It may very well be possible to reconcile socialism with peasantry by precisely such means as were used in the past to reconcile peasantry with land-communism. And first, let us be perfectly clear that there is nothing "fundamental", nothing even very ancient about absolute private ownership of land. It is a system which occurs only rather late in the history of each civilization, and it is a product of corruption and the cynical neglect of equity, of original equality, of original liberty. It is a system imposed by the towns upon the countryside, by the usurer upon the farmer. It can be and it should be abandoned. How? And what is to replace it?

LAND NATIONALIZATION

Quite apart from questions of socialist dogma or of equity, the nationalization of the land is a necessity if we are to create conditions for good farming, because the present owners of land can no longer afford to play their part in farming. Their part was, and is, to maintain buildings, and supply the fundamental facilities of farming, lanes, water, drainage and so forth. It was also the business of the enterprising land-owner to claim for agriculture such of his land as needed clearing and turning into fertile soil. Many great land-owners did such work magnificently. Coke of Holkham, for example, turned a vast area of poor and barren Norfolk land into rich agricultural land. There were many others. But, within our time, the progress first of Liberal and later of Socialist doctrines, has, by taxation and death-duties, so impoverished land-owners that, with the best will in the world, they cannot properly perform their function in the farming complex. It is probable that this has been a mistake: the land-owners, as a class, contributed to the national wealth, and had it not been for one factor, means might have been found to allow them to continue putting their money into the land, while liberalizing and controlling the land-owning system. The factor which made this impossible was the rise of the industrial and mercantile class which, resenting the land-owners' hold on the Government of the nation, contrived to turn the resentment of the working class against the land-owners, and therefore away from themselves, who were to become far more ruthless oppressors of "labour" than the landlords ever were. Thus, the historical function of political Liberalism, too often the reverse of liberal, has been to raise commerce and industry by, as it were, turning the anger of the people against the rural magnates.

However, there is no profit in shaking one's head over the past. Today, we have no alternative to nationalization of the land, a policy advocated even by so great and successful a farmer-owner as Mr. Hosier.[1]

It is not our business to discuss the ways and means of bringing this nationalization about: there are doubtless experts in the Labour Party—the party probably destined to carry through this difficult measure whether they like it or not—who will be competent to devise the proper method and who will be checked if tempted to doctrinaire excesses, by the Conservative Party, which, although actually the party of industry and commerce—for the rural interest is virtually disenfranchised by the little importance it has in voting strength—will do its duty of opposing, when in opposition!

THE STATE AS LANDOWNER

As the land-owner, the Nation will be obliged to put every square yard of available land area into condition to be farmed; to provide such roads, hedges, fences, woods, shelter belts, water supply, electric power, drainage, houses and farm-buildings as are required if the land is to be well-farmed. And, like any other land-owner, the Nation will have to:

[1] See *Hosier's Farming System*, A. J. and F. H. Hosier. (Crosby Lockwood, 1951).

(*a*) Devise a form of agreement with farmer-tenants, satisfactory to both parties.

(*b*) Seek, find and install suitable tenants in its 50 million acres of farms.

These two operations will have to be carried out under at least three different heads:

(1) Coming to agreement with present owner-farmers.

(2) Coming to agreement with present tenant-farmers.

(3) Seeking tenants for vacant farms or for newly-created farms on cleared marginal lands and reclaimed lands.

THE FORM OF AGREEMENT BETWEEN NATION AND FARMERS

It must be in the form of agreement between the Nation and the farmers that we shall incorporate those clauses which will give the farmers, the new peasants, the advantages, and therefore the encouragements, of ownership, and so induce them to husband and not exploit their holdings; and those other clauses which will nevertheless make the new system "socialist" in the best and most sensible meaning of that word. To these ends it must be agreed that the farmer will, by the terms of his lease, be a freeholder in all but one respect: he may not alienate his land either by sale, gift, will or any other means; nor may he raise money on it excepting from the National Farmer's Bank (to be established) and for the purpose of capitalizing his farming work. Otherwise, he will, with certain conditions, be free, and his farm will, also on certain conditions, pass to the heir or heirs of his body. The principal condition of this inheritance—*that such heir or heirs have been reared, trained, educated and apprenticed as farmers with the definite object of succeeding him.*

What is required is to devise a means whereby pride of property and the farmer's desire that his work shall be carried on by his sons and grandsons, be put at the service of the community. As we have already declared, it is not our business to deal with the details of this contract, but there are certain attributes which it must possess. In return for the right to hold his farm and work it, within wide limits in his own way, the farmer will have to agree to maintain a rising value of soil fertility and of crops, in both weight and quality. The Nation will have the right and duty of dispossessing the farmer of his farm upon an unfavourable report of the Land Warden or the Regional Committee. The farmer will have the right to resort to the courts to enforce the law compelling the Nation to drain his land, clear and recover waste land or marginal land within his holding, and maintain buildings and fences, ditches and woods.

A farmer compelled to quit the land for whatever reason will have only one resort: to place his farm at the disposal of the Nation in its representative, the Ministry of Agriculture, or of Land, receiving in compensation the difference in value, assessed on fertility and crop-potential, between his farm when he took it and when he relinquishes it.

A farmer who has no children, or whose children do not wish to farm land, must be obliged to take one or more apprentices and to train them to take on his work exactly as if they were his children. Such apprentices will pass to him from Agricultural Colleges, if he applies for a graduate apprentice, or they may be promoted labourers—foremen or charge-hands. But although every means must be taken to assure this recruitment of master-farmers from among journeymen farmers—that is, agricultural wage-earning workers—such promoted workers will be obliged to give part of their time to technical education, which must be available free, of course, in as large a number of agricultural centres as possible.

The farmer whose children propose to succeed him will have to follow, from the beginning, a suitable course of education. We touch on this in another chapter: it is a question of educating children too young to decide on their future, in such a manner as to turn their minds towards a rural life without closing those minds to other possible ways of life.

As outlined, the system of land-holding sketched above, the object of which is to establish a new, modern peasantry, has two extremely grave faults: it establishes a caste; and it is far too rigid to work well. For example, what room is there for the able and ambitious farmer to expand? Or for the specialist with a strong bent towards a particular branch of farming? Or for the farmer who wants to move? The answer is—we are constructing a framework, not covering it. As to the establishment of a caste, it may be unavoidable and it is not necessarily evil. Equality has been carried too far, and in the wrong direction in modern societies: it is perfectly obvious that primary producers are of far greater value to the Nation than secondary producers or negotiators or record-keepers. A farm-labourer is worth far more than a stockbroker, a fisherman than a lawyer, a coal-miner than a commercial traveller. The most valuable members of any community are unquestionably its farmers, fishermen, miners, craftsmen (or their modern equivalent, pattern-makers), designers, scientific workers, artists, writers and all types of medical worker. But the capitalist-industrialist system pays the gambler and negotiator best in money and power, just as the socialist-industrialist system pays the politician or party organizer. If the caste system we create recognizes as "noble" those occupations which by serving mankind and improving man's inheritance *are* noble, then it may be a social good rather than a social evil.

EXPANSION OF FARMING

It will be the duty of the land-owning Nation to expand agriculture on to every square inch of available or recoverable surface; and, conversely, to *prevent* the expansion of industry, housing, armed forces on to any land which can possibly be used for growing food or raw materials. For we can no longer afford not to put first things first. As our farmers and their auxiliaries, whether scientists or labourers, or that part of industry serving agriculture, will have to become an elite, like our higher Civil Service, so the claim of agriculture to land must be paramount and unquestioned.

Are we, then, to do without houses and to put industry into

a strait-jacket? By no means. We are, at long last, to make use of science and industry in a sensible manner.

A very odd and evil consequence of imperialism has been the almost total failure to apply "science" to large domestic problems. It seems that the most difficult thing for us to do is to look closely, to bring our eyes down a shade, from the horizon to the middle distance and the near. Even overseas our achievements in topographical engineering for agricultural and industrial ends are trivial by comparison with the achievements of the past, when our immense technical superiority is taken into account. With all our power and all our science, we have done nothing to equal the terrace-building of the Incas, the tank-building of the ancient people of Ceylon. We have hardly and rarely surpassed the dam-building feats of the Bronze Age Baluchis of Northern India. Given our means, our achievements have been pitiful, our science timid.

The reason for this has, however, been honourable. Very great works in topographical engineering can only be carried out by whole communities working in concert. When governments command their people, either as slaves, or as free citizens organized under some form of communalism, when they can apply the whole man-power and material resources of a nation to some great work, colossal achievements are possible. Western civilization has, however, given the liberty of the individual so great an importance that mobilization of the people for any great work, excepting war, has never been possible. Private enterprise, however rich and powerful its units may grow, can work only in detail, cannot operate on a scale which takes in scores of different occupations and the whole topography of a region: it has neither the means, nor the rights, over land and people possessed by a government.

It would be better for us to die of starvation than to feed ourselves only at the cost of giving up the Western ideal of the importance and rights of the individual. But there must be some expedient compromise whereby men can be persuaded, not forced, to work in concert; a respect for liberty has so led us to tolerate licence, that we have allowed the liberty of rich and powerful men and corporations to expand at the expense of the liberty of small people.

The Nation must have the right to apply engineering to the homeland as it has applied it in Sind and Egypt and elsewhere. Why must we, with our colossal technical resources, use agricultural land for airports, when the proper place for runways is on the roofs of cities? Or over our coastal waters? Why must our houses, factories and offices continue to engross fertile land at the rate of 50,000 acres per annum, when the Americans have shown us how to build upwards? Why must vast, sprawling, hideous industrial slums continue to mar the face of our country, when by applying power and machinery to clearance, re-planning and rebuilding, our whole industry could be contracted into a quarter of its present space, to the very great advantage of its efficiency, economy, the health of its workers, its output and profit, and to amenity? Why must we build 200,000 houses a year on agricultural land which is thus sterilized, while 200,000 houses a year rot and fall down in our ugly, dirty and inefficient cities?

The answer to these and to innumerable similar questions is fourfold:

(i) An excessive respect for the sacrosanctity of property.

(ii) Inertia due to our tradition of scrounging, looting and trading abroad instead of creative working at home—heritage of the much-praised but ethically and socially vicious Victorians.

(iii) The contemptible quality of political leadership.

(iv) Mis-application of capital, usually covered up by the excuse, "We cannot afford it".

None of these difficulties are real and the only one which looks serious is the last, and that is the most unreal of all. A nation can afford a piece of work for which it has material and labour and power: the cost reckoned in money is of no significance while that money is simply changing hands within the nation. It is being moved from one pocket to another.

It comes to this: we can both make room for more farms and greatly increase the efficiency of industry while increasing housing accommodation by, as it were, rationalizing the use of space, clearing up nineteenth-century messes, and using topographical engineering to alter the face of the country. It is our business to make ourselves comfortable in our island, and it can be done.

NATURE OF MECHANIZED PEASANT FARMING

There is absolutely no need to define the new peasant-holding and describe its working as if only a single pattern is to be copied. A farming system must be flexible. The size of the holding, for example, can only be determined by the kind of farming to be practised in any given region; and that, in its turn, by the topography of the region and its soil. On rich market-garden soil where intensive horticulture can be applied, the holding might be as small as 5 acres. Where the country demands sheep in great numbers and some forestry, it might be as large as 500 acres or more. Our farming, as it actually is, already tends to "express" the diversities of our countryside, and this is a tendency which could and should be encouraged.

There are, however, certain general principles which will have to be accepted, and we will discuss the most important.

"High" farming is farming in which arable farming and stock-raising are combined to support each other, and both practised as intensively as possible. The farm carries the maximum head of the finest possible stock—cattle, sheep, pigs, poultry: the dung of these animals is carefully conserved and used to enrich the arable acres. Much of the stock-feed is grown as a crop, rather than permanent grass, whether for grazing or mowing. The object of "high" farming may be expressed thus: it is to turn over the available capital in soil fertility as often and as fast as possible, while constantly increasing it. It is, in fact, comparable with "good" business.

Such farming produces the largest crops per acre in the

world. But it is expensive, requiring much labour and machinery. The crops, to pay for this kind of farming, must be sold at a relatively high price.

"High" farming was devised and practised in Britain in the 18th and 19th centuries. It was more or less abandoned because the "Liberal" anti-rural industrial interests refused to pay their factory hands decent wages. Consequently, urban populations could not afford to eat at the prices which made high farming profitable. Cheap food was bought abroad by destroying the fertility of America and exploiting half-starved "lesser tribes", and high farming was ruined. This magnificent achievement was a fairly typical product of Victorian industry and enterprise! In short, of rapacity.

The criterion in those days was, then, the price of food in cash (or exports). What should it be today? *The cost of food in acreage of land required to grow it.* The only kind of farming we can afford is, therefore, high farming, intensive farming.

What does this entail? The basing of industrial wages on the true cost of home-grown food. When we have determined what bread, meat and vegetables cost to grow under a system primarily concerned with getting the absolute maximum of crops per acre while maintaining and increasing soil fertility and soil structure, then, on the basis of those figures, we can construct a new cost-of-living index. And on that index industrial wages must be calculated. Undoubtedly, our people will have to learn to spend a higher proportion of their income on food. Whether wages are raised, or the food paid for out of subsidies, is none of our business. However it is done, we have got to afford tons-per-acre farming, not tons-per-man-hour, or tons-per-£1-invested farming.

MECHANIZATION OF THE "PEASANT"

The holdings in our new economy are to be supplied, of course, with mains water and electric power by the land-owner Nation. The farmer himself will own and provide every kind of light machine which is constantly needed on the farm:

electrical milking apparatus, motor-cultivators, tractors, motor-scythes and so forth. But it is not necessary that he should own such heavy machinery as combine-harvesters, sub-soilers, threshing machines. These will be provided by the Co-operative to which the farmer will belong, and those Co-operatives will tend also to own and operate ensilage and grass-drying facilities, gas-stores for fruit, canning and jam-making factories, plant for the extraction and bottling of fruit-juices and the making of cyder and perhaps even wine.

The object must be to relieve the farmer of all commercial and industrial preoccupations, and to place at his disposal the maximum of power and science, to the use of which, however, he will be required to apply judgment based upon sound, soil-conservation traditions.

As we have already written—first things first. And the first thing is food. What we propose is to base our whole economy on the true cost of home-grown food produced by intensive farming from the maximum of crops per acre. It goes without saying that waste and inefficiency will not be tolerated, and that every means must be used to keep the price of crops as low as possible, provided that the output per acre does not suffer. How is this to be achieved? By the well-proved "capitalist" device of competition; by rationalized distribution; by rationalized transport.

As to competition, the peasant Coöperatives will be limited to the regions defined by each Land Ward, and they will, therefore, be numerous. Within the limits set by the rationalization of distribution and transport, the Coöperatives will compete with each other in the market. But the actual distribution will be managed by a super-Coöperative to which the smaller Land Ward Coöperatives will belong. The regions served by these larger bodies will be determined by population density. A principal object must be to sell the crops as near as possible to the farm, and the Coöperatives must not be free to put crops on the market wherever they like, merely to grab a good price. Competition is useful; but it ceases to be effective as a means of price control when it results merely in using up valuable train and truck space, time and power. What counts is not the profits of one trade, but the economy of the nation as a whole.

The success of the new peasant system would depend, in the long run, upon the farmers' success in maintaining and increasing fertility *out of their own resources*. It is perfectly possible to boost crop-yields by an excessive use of chemical fertilizers. But this is not sound, any more than it is sound to win a horse-race by doping the horse. The use of some industrial fertilizers is justified; total dependence on them is not—especially when they have to be imported, or the materials for them imported. Our farms must become, as nearly as possible, self-supporting. This, therefore, is the subject of our next chapter.

H. J. Massingham

CHAPTER VIII

A Self-supporting Soil

AT THE beginning of Chapter IV, we stressed the fact that both our civilization and the situation in which we now find ourselves as the result of the former's exorbitant development, bristle with paradoxes. We have now reached the point when one of the most glaring of these paradoxes demands closer attention. For it leads us on to a conclusion of the greatest importance and is concerned with the earth itself from which we draw the sustenance of our being.

Our history during the 19th century and the early part of the 20th discloses an attitude of mind so dominant as to be unmistakable when we look back upon it. It was one of immeasurable pride in material achievement, a pride distinct from that of Renaissance man who prided himself rather on his culture, on his liberation from former restraints and obligations and on the full flowering of his individuality as a person. The pride in material power and expansion is of a different order, and indeed has ended in the depression or suppression of the individual as a person. It might be called the pride of Lucifer, the Light-Bringer, the light that was kindled from the nether fires of coal and iron. But in the intoxication of this pride it entirely escaped notice that it was founded and grounded upon a situation of which we should be anything but proud; founded and grounded, that is to say, upon the ignoble fact of parasitism. The proud heir of all the ages who believed that he stood at the head of the inevitable march of progress, and who had created "the workshop of the world" and a wealth that took the shine out of Midas, had made his pile in no other way than as a parasite. This it was left to us to discover when optimism had fallen out of fashion and the effects of parasitism were beginning to be felt.

After the Repeal of the Corn Laws in the middle of last century, we became in full what we had previously been in part, a parasitic nation. After the Great Depression of 1879, the logical consequence of such parasitism, we left our own countryside to go to the dogs. In the name of progress, it went back to what it had been before the first Belgic ox-plough broke its sod, a country of virgin forest and meadowland, the only difference being that the forest was now scrub and the meadowland arable reverted to grass. Again, in 1939, when the feeding-tube between ourselves and the agricultural resources of the outside world was about to be severed, we became perforce what with an entirely unconscious irony we agreed to call ourselves—a self-supporting nation—once more. What we actually did was to cash in on the fertility that had accumulated in the soil during the sixty years when the plough was rusting, and nature by her own processes of humus-manufacture was building up the reserves under the grass for us to spend and largely dissipate in six years. Whether any alternative was open to us in such threatening circumstances is not the point. This was what happened. Each of these three events—the killing of the home-market in wheat by the imported cheap grain of the North American prairies, now a dust-bowl; the abandonment of our countryside to become a picturesque ruin from the 'seventies onward, and the exploitation of the resources nature had year by year been forming, gathering and enriching—each section of this triple series was a stage in the growth of parasitism. Whether we fed off the fat of our own land or off that of other people's, the only difference was that parasitism began abroad and ended at home. As Rome had done before us, so we did.

But that is not the whole of the story. We have been not merely robbing nature of her capital—namely, her humus whereby vegetation and animal life are maintained in a state of equilibrium—but our own children, since they, no less than ourselves, must depend upon that natural capital to keep them alive. In fact, the highway robbery of our industrial civilization from nature and her cultivators in the name of trade and competition has throughout been entirely impartial and indiscriminate. The very seas are being fished out as the land is being farmed out, the virgin forest felled, the fertile wild turned to wilderness. It is pretty well known now in Britain what the United States did with North America, how by 1937 the fertility of 61% of the entire land-surface, or 253 million acres, had been wholly or partly destroyed, how night took the place of midday in New York and Washington because the skies were full of drifting earth, of soil-particles blown as dust over hundreds of miles. But when thousands of ship-loads of the wheat grown on those acres were unloaded at our ports as the "cheap food" of our economic system, we can hardly acquit ourselves of having been accomplices in the greatest crime of rapine the natural world has ever known.

Nor has the commercial rapacity of that system, whose buccaneer days are now numbered, been confined to the Americas, as anybody who turns the pages of *The Rape of the Earth*, by G. V. Jacks and R. O. Whyte,[1] can verify for himself. The authors tell us that between 1914 and 1938 more soil was lost to the world than in the whole previous history of mankind; a rape, vast quantities of whose booty reached our shores, whether from Kansas or Kenya, whether from the ranches of Australia or the cotton plantations of Alabama and Louisiana. For the "cheap food" for which our children will pay so dear, and we ourselves likely enough with our hungry lives, is only one item in the great account. Where did the raw materials come from that filled our warehouses, broke up our rural culture, set the machines on the roar, shot up our factories, shot out our arterial roads, defiled our countryside and created our proletariat of landless men? Where but from the earth, and by precisely the same methods of getting something for nothing (politely called "the profit motive") which blew or washed away the topsoil of millions of acres in the cause of cheap food. Certainly we are not alone in the dock of history;

[1] Faber, 1939.

our fellow-criminals are beside us. But let it not be forgotten that we, "the workshop of the world", exchanging our manufactures for the cheap food of cheap labour in stolen goods, the very stuff of life dragged out of the lap of nature, were the first in the field.

If what created our industrial civilization has been the wedding of pride with parasitism, so behind the respectable mask of the cosmopolitan citizen is the face of an outlaw who has lived by what Shakespeare called "commodity". In Falconbridge in *King John*, but yet more fittingly in Edmund in *King Lear*, we see ourselves in the mirror of our industrial civilization.

How was this incredible victory, this "conquest of nature", accomplished? By the armament of science. It is impossible for us to understand the enigma of modern technical science, which carried the world to such giddy heights of material progress and now threatens to shatter it to bits, unless we clearly realize that by its own act and volition it has bound itself by a kind of Faustian pact to industrialism. Science created industrial civilization and in so doing committed itself irrevocably to the vast but one-idea'd edifice it had raised. What has been its creation is also its prison.

We have only to compare the work of pre-industrial, with that of post-industrial science to grasp what a radical difference there is between the two. Pre-industrial science was less accurate in its measurements than ours, and it did not know anything like so much about the building materials of the universe. But it knew more about the universe as a whole; it was far more comprehensive in its mentality, far more liberal in outlook, far less confined in range than ours. It tried to take in the whole man, the universality of nature, the meaning of the whole scheme of things, the values as well as the quantities, the spirit as well as the flesh, the feeling as well as the fact. Nor was it so completely isolated from religious apprehensions as ours has become.

But the Faustian bond of modern science has excluded all

the imponderables, all that cannot be weighed and measured into physical or mathematical categories, as irrelevant or subject to them. It has thus made a partition in the nature of man and a division in the study of nature. And so the penalty it has had to pay is to lose the whole in the part, to analyse the trees very correctly, but to lose sight of the wood. The defect of modern science is its fragmentation, its multitude of separate studies not only unrelated to one another but devoid of significance by each part being shut up in its own exclusive little compartment. But no part can have any real meaning except in association with its own proper whole. A part aping a whole is something counterfeit, a deception, an error, however exact and logical its analysis. By over-specialization science abandoned its birthright of free enquiry into truth. Truth itself has ceased to exist, squeezed out between measurement and quantity.

By this process of attrition, the concept of nature suffered as much as did the natural world of life by the scientific and industrial plunder of its fertility. In the province of science we deal with in this book, soil came to be regarded as an inert substance capable of unlimited exploitation and (illogically) whose depletion of reserves could always be made good by chemical substitutes. At the same time, the organic life of nature was translated into mechanical terms, but was also represented as a blind and internecine struggle for dominance between species, in which the weakest went to the wall and the efficient flourished and multiplied. In other words, the biological world of nature was viewed by the Darwinian theory as an extension on a larger scale of the industrial world of man in which the weakest went to the wall, and the more efficient in taking advantage of the profit motive flourished and made fortunes.

It was the unification of these dual concepts—the idea of soil as exploitable dead matter and of organic life as a continuous struggle for existence that fostered the so successful and so disastrous scientific idea of "the conquest of nature". What they both left out was the total *environment* of soil, plant, animal and man in a given landscape. That is the province of the ecologist, who is somebody much more than a scientist, and fundamentally an artist and a philosopher. He restores the lost concept of wholeness and so really does "hold the mirror up to Nature". He is the only counter to the scientific idea of conquering nature, and it is to him we must go in the parting of the ways that lies immediately ahead. We do not go to the housebreaker for insurance against burglary.

*

The question, therefore, spontaneously arises—which view of nature is the most to be trusted, the scientific-commercial-industrial view to which the vast majority of our present population adheres, or that of the ecologist, a novelty who has only just made his appearance on the stage, and the traditional peasant who has been booed off the stage as a type of farmer as obsolete as the dodo in his canons of good husbandry? This indeed is the crucial issue, for on which side we pin our faith depends our survival as a nation. We have already discussed in previous chapters what the approaches and the methods of the latter party are, and from them we may deduce that the ecologist's and the peasant's view of nature are in every possible way the reverse of that of the party which now holds the field and governs the national policy towards the land which is to support us lest we perish.

Two lines of enquiry are thus open to us: we can assess, first, what has been the effect on nature of the prevailing view and, secondly, whether the observation of nature as a whole or as a series of self-contained wholes bound together in a general unity, does in fact lend countenance to and justify the attitude of the ecologist and the peasant. The first of these questions has already been answered in part by the shattering facts of soil-erosion and infertility covering hundreds of millions of acres throughout the land-surface of our planet. To them we have to add the mounting multitudes of pests, viruses and diseases which decimate our crops and have become so alarming a feature of modern agriculture that of the fifteen committees set up between the wars by the Agricultural Research Council, no fewer than twelve were for the investigation of plant-diseases.

The fantastically rapid development of more and more lethal fungicides and insecticides, the increase of spraying poisons for fruit trees and bushes from once a year to seven times within the last decade, the obsession of what Sir Albert Howard called "the laboratory hermit" with bacteriological counter-attacks against the insurgence of the noxious hosts that now prey upon the crops—this is further evidence that the conquest of nature is not proceeding according to plan. The process is hydra-headed. Chop one head off the monster, and three appear in its place. Somewhere or other there is a fatal misconception of the way that nature works, a faultiness of observation as to nature's system of maintaining health and fertility in soil and plant and animal, a fundamental error, too, in our philosophic attitude to nature.

We can discover how and where the modern world has blundered off the path of truth only by carrying our observations of the ecologist and the peasant in action a little further. Britain's primary objective must be to become a self-supporting nation; the ecologist studies the self-supporting landscape and region, while the peasant's idea and practice of husbandry is the self-supporting farm:

> I eat my own Lamb,
> My chickens and Ham,
> I shear my own fleece and I wear it,

as the old farming catch ran. In order to complete the cycle, we have to find out whether in fact the soil itself does, or does not, conduct its affairs on self-supporting principles. For, if it does so, the ideas and the methods of the ecologist and the peasant are completely vindicated.

Here is the real answer to that parasitism and rapacity which have distinguished the industrial age, for both in unequivocal terms run directly counter to the self-supporting nation, region, farm and garden. When the modern farmer rings up his agent and orders a bag of oil-cake or other concentrates, he is simply transferring fertility from one place to another, and most of modern commercial farming is conducted by this perpetual exchange of buying in, and selling off, fertility until the consumer finally disposes of it and the residues are hurried away to the sea. Wherever we turn, the idea of a cycle of give and take, of the return of all wastes to replace what is spent, the idea of a piece of land being self-supporting in itself, is violated.

The subject of soil-population—of the micro-organisms, micro-flora, yeasts and fungi that live in the soil and are invisible except to the microscope—is one of great complexity. Even today, the investigations of the Soil Association, the only body that concerns itself with soil as a living complex, have penetrated rather than opened up this unknown territory. Nevertheless, it is certain that these hordes of bacteria, tens of millions of them to a spoonful and weighing for all their minuteness as much as 40 tons to the acre, are as essential in the formation of humus as the earthworm itself, and that the greater their variety and density, the better the quality of the humus. This prodigious "unpaid labour force", as Sir Albert Howard called it, is engaged with the utmost nicety and differentiation of function in breaking up or decomposing all forms of wastes and residues that reach the soil, whether manurial or otherwise, and of every imaginable kind of living substance, into that "crumb-structure" of the soil which supports plant-life and, through the plant, both animal and human life.

But these bacteria are really architects of soil, for the crumbs on the surface, distinct, and so admitting air and water, are smaller particles gummed together by a by-product of certain of these tiny functionaries and supported on long columns or shafts of soil with arterial roads and lanes between them made by the worms and roots of the plants. Nor do these activities exhaust bacterial capacity for making soil a congenial home for the plant, since workers of other genera are occupied in establishing vital relations with the fibrous rootlets of the plants themselves, a relationship which is not parasitic but symbiotic; that is, mutually beneficial both to plant and animalcule.

This intricate and marvellously coördinated series of biological processes is in perpetual cyclical operation throughout the whole organic kingdom of nature. In the man-made compost-stack we see a tightened-up, quickened and intensified shorthand version of it, while in the reclamation of Australian desert conditions, symbiotic bacteria have actually been bred in cultures in conjunction with plant-roots to foster their growth and build up a biological resistance to drought and sterility. Being an adaptation derived from the natural cycle, well-made compost is the very quiddity of fertile soil, the life-stuff that makes the world of organic nature go round. It is going round all the time in the wheel-like procession of decay, death, germination, growth, maturity, decline and again decay and death. No process is separable from its neighbour and, if the end of life is death, death is the beginning of a new life sprung from it.

As we know from the record of the rocks, soil was first created and is being continuously created by the agencies of fire, water, frost, ice, air, wind and attrition from the rock-bones of the earth; by the forces, that is to say, of denudation. Both from this primordial soil and from the sun and air and water, plants take what they need—nitrogen, phosphorus, calcium, trace-elements—everything from inorganic nature except life. The difference, therefore, between the subsoil scraped off the rocks and the topsoil swarming with bacteria, earthworms and other forms of life, is that the one is a reservoir of life and the other is lifeless. The life is on top in a double sense: it alone can secure that cyclical continuity which maintains plant-life and its descendants in health and vigour; and the living substance that thus perpetually asserts the final word is humus. The ingredients taken from sun, air, water and subsoil are indispensable accessories, but only as utilized by life for its own ends. It is the living plant that by its leaves traps and converts the sunlight, and through its roots captures the trace-elements in the subsoil. But the coöperation between the living plant and the living soil, the balance and circulation of functions between them, this is the dominant and decisive factor of natural life and the human life that depends on it. By it, subsoil is itself converted into topsoil.

Jacquetta Hawkes in *A Land*,[1] has commented on the farmer's expression of a field "in good heart": "It is no empty sentimental term, for the structure of the soil depends on this organic contribution, and it is a quality that cannot be given by artificial fertilizers." Natural fertility is derived from humus, and humus is what the ecologist, Dr. Pfeiffer, has called "the source of all land-life", the soil's living capital and so "the alpha and omega of soil culture". The manufacture of that crumb structure which is the indication of a soil rich in humus is dependent in its turn upon a highly developed system of communication within the soil, the work both of earthworms and of countless bacteria which are the true cultivators, while the worm-burrows are the main channels for air and water to be carried down to the deeper layers. When the peasant or the gardener returns all the wastes of his land to the soil whether in the form of compost or manurial residues, he is feeding not the plants but the micro-organisms that provide the plant-food. Yet all you will hear of this from the agricultural scientist is that humus, or what he calls "organic matter", which is not the same thing, is useful in the retention of moisture. For, to him the farm is merely the workshop of the laboratory.

Both the processes and the properties of this highly complex biological interdependence are still, as we have said, imperfectly understood. But what is known does point decisively to the fact that fertility, nutrition and health are not a set of distinctive "problems" but indispensable parts of a coherent whole

[1] Cresset Press, 1951.

based on humus, itself the product of that cyclical motion between life and death which in agricultural parlance we call the return of all wastes. Since another set of bacteria acts as checks and antidotes to disease-parasites, humus does confer, if not immunity, a very high degree of disease-resistance,[1] and fertility itself does raise the nutritive value of food grown in a fertile soil.

A further property is that the act of creating humus is incessant, so that, though samples taken from an organic plot may not contain as much plant-food as from one heavily dosed with "fertilizers", the actual supply is being produced and released continuously. It thus responds to the needs of the plant through every stage of growth and maturity from the germination of the seed. A stream of "nutrients" is in circulation all the time and this tends to make the scientific "soil test" deceptive because such a test registers soil conditions only at one particular moment. It follows that, if the biological balance is maintained, if all the parts in the intricate life-pattern are working smoothly, if the cycle is unbroken at every point, there is a perennial normality of fertility and so of health.

Do we not *know* it to be so? But for the accidents, say, of an earthquake or change of climate or, what is much more likely, man arriving on the scene with his death-dealing profit motive, a virgin mixed forest can live on its own fat—to wit, its own leaf-fall, its bird-droppings, the life-and-death succession of the fauna of the forest floor—to world's end in an indefinite process of self-regeneration and by the very instruments of decay and death which renew and guarantee its continuity of life.

In respect of grass, Dr. Paul Sears[2] has shown that the humus content of the prairie fulfils every function. The prairie reaches a stable, change-resistant "climax" when "the resources of soil and plant are at their richest" by tempering the soil against extremes of wet or dry, absorbing and holding water like a sponge and preventing it from scouring away the soil, adjusting

[1] For instance, the eel-worm, which is the scourge of our potato fields, is comparatively innocuous in a humus-rich soil.

[2] *Deserts on the March* (Routledge and Kegan Paul, 1939).

the different species of plant and animal to one another, relating them to their physical environment and producing as healthy and varied an abundance of life as the region will hold. The conclusion states itself—that in the right conditions which can be made or marred by man, a given area of soil, whether on a farm or in a garden or an ecological region, can be, and very often is, fully self-supporting. It is capable of becoming an autonomous, self-acting whole without any external aids or props at all, excepting only air and sunlight and the subsoil probed by the deep-rooting trees, herbs and grasses.

It seems to us that this conclusion goes further than justifying the ecologist as an observer and the peasant as a farmer, further even than revealing the only safe and sure way of escaping famine. Soil, farmer, land-warden, the nation itself—to become self-supporting we have to follow the implications of the term to its sources. We can potter and fumble with the issue by pretending to become self-supporting on the basis of the factory-farm and the chemical laboratory, or we can become so in reality through all the stages from clod to community. If the latter, there are overtones to be considered which involve more than security against hunger, a very sharp rise in the standard of nutrition and a corresponding decline in that invalidism of soil, plant, animal and man which is so marked a feature of our time. Our endeavours will be blessed and made fruitful by a new, sane and positive attitude to nature. For it will become evident that the modern attitude to nature as a blind clash of predatory forces, as a machine to be handled and driven at high velocity, as a repository of wealth to be exploited and as an enemy to be conquered, is a misleading and a superficial one.

In *Landscape into Art*,[1] Sir Kenneth Clark remarked that the virtual disappearance of landscape-painting and pastoral poetry in our age was due to the bleak, forbidding and terrifyingly incomprehensible picture of nature given us by modern

[1] Murray, 1949.

science. But surely the boot is on the other foot. It is because the modern world has wrenched itself apart from nature in its urban habitat, its industrial pursuits and its scientific over-specialization, that we have acquired an altogether distorted view of what nature is really like. Leaving out of account the fact that nature continues to stir the aesthetic emotions, whether we dismiss them as "the pathetic fallacy" or not, we cannot ignore the investigation of the humbler elements of life in the soil, the peasant's and ecologist's attentiveness to the needs of mixed farming and the highly developed interchange between vegetable and animal life, between the organic and the inorganic, as disclosing a very different picture. A picture of wholeness, of the coördination of parts, of measure and order, which is much nearer the pre-industrial concept of nature as a system of natural law than it is to T. H. Huxley's "gladiatorial show".

A man can breathe in this morning air a deep breath of deliverance from a nightmare pseudo-philosophy built up not from nature but from the completely unnatural conditions of the industrial age. He feels no longer cut off irrevocably from a past which at one time saw nature in the figure of the Great Mother of fertility; at another, with the eyes of Job, as the mighty handiwork of the Creator; at another, as the environment and the very speech of Shakespeare, that great countryman; at others, as the Van Eycks depicted it and poet and peasant alike celebrated it in song, dance and the written word. King Lear said: "Is there any cause in Nature that makes these hard hearts?" There are two ways of answering this question, but for a century and more there had been only one.

*

It is obvious that this chain of self-subsistence and mutual aid up from the soil to the plant and animal, from the farm to the region and through the region to the nation, has now completely broken down. Every link in the chain has snapped. The soil has become so impoverished that it is unable to go on bearing sufficient crops without a stream of chemical "nutrients" in larger and larger quantities flowing into it from the laboratory and the factory, while at places even in England it gives up altogether and is blown or washed away.[1] Where a disease in plant or animal has been cured by chemical action, another promptly takes its place. To what extent plant and animal metabolisms are changed by repeated doses of fertilizers, "systemic" insecticides, synthetic hormones and antibiotics, nobody knows and few enough care. Health, that is to say resistance to sickness, is abandoned in favour of eliminating the latter by ever deadlier venoms, so that the farm has become a hospital; its crops and stock, patients in it.

At the same time, the farm has become an export firm, selling off all or most of its produce and receiving in exchange, not the wealth of wastes that renews fertility, but money only, the money that buys anything except the organic food for want of which the land starves. The region in its turn is drawn into the vortex of centrality, while the nation still hangs desperately to the phantom illusion that the outside world possesses the means and the will to supply it with what it has not enough of for itself, quite apart from the prohibitive cost of what was once "cheap food" from abroad.

If anybody from university don to factory hand thinks it possible for us to avert starvation on such terms as these, let him think again. What is the reply of agricultural science and economics? Artificial insemination,[2] and plant and animal breeding, for one; fertilizers, "hormones", "antibiotics" and all the subsidized ingenuity of inorganic research, for another; "protection and control" by chemical weapons against pests, fungi, viruses and weeds and a great increase in chemical fertilizers, for a third; stepping up production, for a fourth; stimulating the export trade ("export or die") as we stimulate the soil, for a fifth; peering anxiously about the world's land-surface for some more exploitable virgin territory, for a sixth;

[1] Viz. in parts of the Fens.

[2] Which entirely cuts out courtship in the natural world.

bargaining in the market of a world food-shortage, for a seventh; planting leys of only a very few artificial grasses and clovers, for the last. A pretty programme!

One and all assume that you can meet an entirely novel situation, one indeed that is unprecedented in modern civilization and flatly contradicts its ideas, methods and practices, simply by tinkering with and reconditioning the *status quo*. You might as well advise a tipsy man who is staggering to the edge of the pier to pull himself together and walk straight. These counter-measures are a fatal example of fragmentation; they see a terrific challenge in bits and pieces, not as a whole, in effects not causes, in terms of today not tomorrow, of the falling leaf not the tree. What they miss is that a nation cannot become self-supporting by necessity without, by an act of will, looking into the meanings and methods of self-support. It is not much use repairing a top-heavy building without foundations by additions to the superstructure. Our soil can support us in one way only, by bringing it back to life both above and below the surface.

If soil is a living entity, if humus is the key to fertility, if it is a consequence of the cycle of life and, in Dr. Pfeiffer's words, "a healthy landscape is a self-renewing, balanced, stable and beautiful organism", it follows that there is an incalculable element in both humus and fertility. If humus is created by the return of all wastes and is the effect of a balance and complex of biological factors, it follows that the application of fixed amounts of chemicals as "plant-foods" has nothing to do with it and is not the answer to fertility. They may, and do stimulate plant-growth and increase the quantity of any given crop. But, being substitutes for an organic process, a short-circuiting of the life-cycle in terms of not-life, they both ignore quality and interfere with the biological balance. This is a common sense that we may claim without presumption to be endorsed by nature when the ultimate effect of the interruption is to unbalance the normal soil conditions and the nutrition dependent on them. Disease, that is to say, is the red light of the depletion of organic reserves and the breaking of the biological round. And since soil, plant, animal and man are all bound together in the nutritive cycle, that disease or lowering of vitality must inevitably, like a stone thrown into the middle of a pond, affect in widening circles the whole order of life.

That is by no means to deny the utility of chemical agents in agriculture as in medicine. To quote one example out of several, we use, and very properly, Burgundy mixture to prevent leaf-curl in peaches. But unless we totally ignore nature's ways of going to work, we do not confuse fertilizers with fertility, with which they have nothing whatever to do. Chemistry has a perfectly legitimate place in agriculture so long as, like the cobbler, it sticks to its last—which is certainly not to feed either soil or plants. It can replace trace-elements where they are missing, but that is a very different thing from providing plants with sham food out of a bag. Yet, if we do become a self-supporting nation in the future, artificial fertilizers have a considerable part to play. Louis Bromfield, who has written a number of books about the organic reclamation of his Malabar Farm in Ohio, has shown the way. The value of such fertilizers to him as an organic farmer has been that of increasing the yields of certain crops by slow-acting chemical stimulation, in order thereby to multiply the wastes for his fields and so restore them to a life exhausted by years of predatory farming.

Unfortunately, the theory invented by the chemist, Liebig, in the 'fifties of last century, that the co-partnership between the soil and its creatures could be ignored and the organic food of plants replaced by minerals, has proceeded to such extravagant lengths that it has acquired a dreadful momentum of its own. When the part becomes the whole, there is the devil to pay. The fragmentary and subdivided approach of agricultural science, its attachment to industrialism and separation from nature, the ebbing of skilled labour from the countryside and the dominance of the machine and the city, all had their effect in blinding a whole age to the fact that its new chemical technology had become an obsession, an infatuation exceeding all bounds, a kind of madness. The constant warnings of nature, becoming more and more dramatic and disastrous in what they revealed—namely, that the whole biological system was being dislocated and the fertility balance was heavily overdrawn—were unable to shake the delusion. Even the massive tragedy of world-wide soil-erosion has not induced orthodox science and commercial agriculture to examine its own credentials.

That insect-pests build up immunity to particular poisons, as, for instance, the blue tick does to arsenic; that predators like ladybirds were equally killed off with their prey by lethal sprays and dusts; that the useful bee and bird were implicated with the fate of the noxious—the only answer was to increase the potency of the venoms to compensate for the failure of their predecessors. Extremely toxic new inventions like Pestox and Parathion have appeared, together with certain sprays and weed-killers that have become so highly efficient at their job as to take to killing not merely insects but men, unless gas-masked like ghouls and fitted out like fiends. It made no difference that DDT was found in the milk and butter-fat of cows, that sulphate of ammonia disposes of the earthworms and benzene hexachloride (BHC) eliminates the micro-organisms in the soil and drastically reduces the micro-flora. The biochemist[1] to the Tobacco Pest Central Research Scheme in Southern Rhodesia has himself said that "heavy annual doses of DDT and BHC appear to have a definite danger of reducing the productivity of soils . . . within a comparatively few years". The answer given to such uncomfortable joltings in the path of victory's triumphal car was to increase the spraying of fields with venomous weed-killers from half a million acres in 1949 to between 3 and 4 millions in 1951.

Perhaps it would be unfair to expect the laboratory scientist who has no personal contact with them to understand the workings of nature. He is hardly the man to get dirt on his

[1] C. J. Shepherd.

shoes. But at least it might have occurred to him to ask the question whether, since crops grown in the fields are consumed by human beings, the poisons with which they are dosed so liberally might not accompany them. Actually, the position is far worse than the dangerous consequences of his being unable to put two and two together. A terrifying article,[1] by Sir Edward Mellanby, F.R.S., formerly Secretary of the Medical Research Council, was published in *The Observer* in May, 1952, in which he described the processing, "improving" and doctoring of human foodstuffs in order (the profit motive again) to disguise the fact that such foods are entirely different from what they pretend to be. According to the Delaney Committee set up by the United States Senate in 1950, there were no fewer than 704 of these chemical substances—preservatives, emulsifiers, "additives", colouring agents, flavours of all kinds, flour "improvers" and bleachers, anti-staling, anti-rancid and sweetening agents, anti-oxidants and antiseptics. None of them have the smallest food-value, and out of the 704, 276 were not "harmless". Some of them produce cancer and hysteria in animals and none of them are immune, as we mentioned in a former chapter, from the suspicion of being toxic. No wonder, then, that we live in a world of invalids, with an annual national ill-health bill of £450,000,000!

The well-known facts that white sugar has nothing left in it but carbohydrates when it has passed through the factory and refinery, and that the roller-mill removes the fluorine, the bran and the wheat-germ from the grain as nature grew it, in order to make the starch only of the national loaf—these scandals that seem to any honest man the vilest of deceptions—pale into peccadilloes before such wholesale cheating as described by Magnus Pyke[2] and publicized by Sir Edward Mellanby.[3]

[1] Reviewing *Townsman's Food*, by Magnus Pyke. (Turnstile Press, 1952).

[2] op. cit.

[3] "To base our nutritional policy on our present rudimentary and mostly chemical knowledge of dietetics and, in particular, to denature foods, and to claim to restore them by the addition of a few laboratory-made vitamins, has always seemed to us an example of hubris that may yet be fittingly chastised." *Medical Press and Circular*.

If, then, chemical science and modern industry are not above taking the risk of poisoning the population for profit, are we not fools indeed to trust them with our fields, our only source of life in the immediate future?

*

This correlation between finding dangerous counterfeits for the natural cycle and dangerous counterfeits for the nutritional cycle, between food as it is grown and food as it is consumed, is more than a dual example of the inorganic bias peculiar to our civilization. It shows, if only by sinning against both, that there *is* an intimate connection between food as grown and food as eaten. There is an exact parallel between the return of all wastes for the health of the fields and keeping intact the wholeness and freshness of foods for the health of the consumer, just as there is a parallel between drugs and patent medicines for the soil and drugs and patent medicines for the consumer's food. Wholeness, heal, health, good Saxon words, are all derived from the same root-word. Freshness, of course, is destroyed by our system of centralization and elaborate transport: in fact, we actually think more of food which has travelled a thousand miles than that which has travelled only ten. Yet through all the ages our agricultural environment has been food grown under good natural conditions and consumed within the neighbourhood. Up to the industrial era the nutrition of man and the fertility of nature have always been inseparable—and there is no more telling argument for re-organizing our entire way of life on a regional basis.

Of late years, figures like Sir Robert McCarrison and bodies like the Peckham Health Centre and that issuing the Cheshire Medical Testament have insisted that there is something in the quality of foods not accounted for by their known chemical ingredients or the calculation of available "nutrients". Quality is the child of freshness and wholeness, and health is a quality of things, like the bloom on a cow's coat, not a mere absence of disease, nor the presence of a certain number of "calories". Quality in some measure reduces the need of quantity, and the veriest idiot will soon know that there is not enough food to go round for our population; impoverished soil means poor quality and so bad health both in nature and in man. Pick and eat an apple off your own tree, grown in normal and natural conditions, and it will do you more good than a dozen wrapped up in tissue paper, inoculated by a preservative and transported from the Antipodes.

There can be no more scathing indictment of our civilization than the mere mention of these obvious home-truths, these elementary platitudes; and yet, before the threat of starvation raised its Medusa-head in our midst, the man who uttered these ABC commonplaces was regarded as an eccentric, a wilful vagrant from the civilized norm, or at best a perverse idealist. The norm has been, and still is, turning real and beneficial food into sham and deleterious food. The norm has been, and still is, judging food not by its quality nor even its taste but by its colours. The norm has been, and still is, such dishonesty in the treatment of food before it reaches the consumer as in the pre-industrial eras was punished as a criminal offence.

But at least in this, the eleventh hour, we can hardly fail of a dawning realization that the industrial system has brought us within an ace of famine. It has caused us first to desert and then to abuse our own countryside on which we now have to depend; it has lured away into the cities the hardy race of cultivators who produced the food from it; it has greatly diminished the area of cultivable land which can produce food; it has broken the old law of the return of wastes by which nature creates humus for sustaining plant-life and maintaining the health not only of the plant but the animals and men it feeds. It still further tampers with the cycle of nutrition by which food is consumed with all its values intact. In parts of China a square mile of cultivated land has by the completest return of all wastes been feeding for many years 1,783 persons; in the United States, a square mile of cultivated land can feed only 61 persons, while in contemporary England no account is taken of the loss of fertility in the costing of mechanized farms. The only rational conclusion is that we must change this system or die, and there is precious little time in which to do so. But if it could not be done, there would be no point in writing this book.

Obviously, so short a book, written by a pair of authors who can only touch upon certain aspects of a monumental theme demanding the skilled attention of all thinking people, must fall short of anything but an introduction to it. Our previous chapters have attempted to open up the issue of the proper utilization of land and the re-establishment of the peasant who, of all types of cultivator, is the least likely to exploit natural reserves and disregard the principles of good husbandry in conserving fertility and restoring the tradition of mixed farming. It is not our business to put forward suggestions as to how the food-racket in adulteration (worse than the Black Market, which at least is illegitimate) can be scotched, or to discuss the limitation of cities so that they can conform with Ivor Brown's definition,[1] "A well-sized city is one that rides easily on the countryside, assisting, not sapping, the villages." These and other issues of like dimensions relevant to our theme might well fill whole books in themselves. Here we are concerned simply with potential and practical means to the cardinal end of rebuilding the fertility of our depleted soils. If we are to become self-supporting, this primary need is beyond dispute.

Clearly, one such means is to organize on a national scale the manufacture of sewage sludge, town refuse and municipal composting. Maidenhead, Leatherhead and a handful of other towns already make and sell their own sludge for spreading on the fields, and what is possible for the pioneer should be obligatory on every town of 10,000 citizens and more, in Britain. Except by the abolition of our present sewage-disposal system in favour of the earth-closet—and this cannot be called

[1] *Summer in Scotland* (Collins, 1952).

practicable—there is no other way of checking the appalling annual wastage of millions of tons of potential fertility by sewers and down the polluted rivers to the sea. Here is one way of partially reversing the incessant and excessive drain in fertility the city inflicts upon the country. Allied to this major reform are the minor ones of cutting and composting the marginal strips of our roadsides, all that is not usable for hay, and the coastal collection of seaweed for farms near the sea. Our coasts annually produce at least 200,000 tons of seaweed, invaluable as an organic fertilizer and as fodder for livestock. And how many thousand tons of fish-residues are wasted yearly instead of going on the fields? It has been calculated that 300,000 men (and we shall soon have that number of unemployed) could be engaged upon the manufacture of humus alone in one way and another, one man for every 100 acres at the rate of 5 tons per acre. That is not enough, but it is better than nothing.

Equally must our farmers receive every facility for re-converting their farms into organic wholes. There are many examples of this change-over in action today, and it is nonsense to say that there has been or need be, if the process is gradual, any heavy drop in yields. One such example is that of Mr. S. Mayall, who farms near Shrewsbury; he has recently taken to the conservation of all waste material (particularly urine, which the up-to-date cowsheds waste more often than not), making compost, planting long-year, deep-rooting leys (see later), shallow ploughing, discing or rotary-cultivating—that is, churning up the topsoil to receive organic wastes, together with the use of a subsoiler to break up "hard pan" (the impervious layer between topsoil and subsoil)—mixed stocking and the planting of seeds from plants organically grown for at least three generations. None of these methods were complicated nor costly, and Mr. Mayall's 600-acre farm was converted in three-and-a-half years without increase of cost and by buying in only 5 tons of slow-acting complete fertilizer and 10 tons of muriate of potash, together with feeding-stuffs for the pigs and some bran, fishmeal, seaweed meal and beans for the cows.

Apart from these, the farm became self-supporting within this short period, with satisfactory yields, a bound forward in the quality of the produce and health of the livestock, a marked increase of clover in the leys and the elimination of all disease except a little wireworm and blight among the potatoes. Let Mr. Mayall speak for himself:

> What I have tried to show is that there is nothing to fear in applying organic principles to a large farm run on commercial lines and to affirm my belief that in these principles lies the only hope of restoring the exhausted soils of much of our agricultural land to fertility, and of checking and finally overcoming most disease problems. I can truthfully say that I have already much to be thankful for and no cause to regret the day when I decided to adopt an all-organic policy.

Another convert, Mr. E. M. Halblieb, one of the leaders of United Farmers of America, testified before the Federal Security Administration in 1950 that in a period of nine years he had raised the yields per acre of his 183-acre farm in Ohio as follows—oats from 30 to 62 bushels, "corn" (maize?) from 40 to 80 bushels and wheat from 26 to 40 bushels, all without sprays or fertilizers, without even lime or phosphate. He declared that the object of "United Farmers" had been "to save this nation from the grave".

Where the excellent open-air bail or electric fence system of evenly and intensively manuring a field with cow-dung does not prevail, the covered yards of our forefathers for wintering cattle should be revived in order to tread the muck and straw, no longer burned nor sold off the farm, and to spread this over the fields in spring. We are assuming that in this regenerated agriculture the farms will be properly manned: even today Captain Wilson's organic farm of 300 acres at Surfleet employs 33 men, 16 women and 9 boys, besides using 11 horses. But the more muck-shifting and spreading is mechanized the better, so that every encouragement should be given to the engineers to turn out self-propelled or tractor-driven machines like the Rapier Ransome Muck-shifter. Another machine that every farm larger than a small-holding should possess, or, in our new scheme, every Coöperative, is the subsoiler whose blade pierces and breaks up the "hard pan", caused by loss of humus which prevents the roots of plants from combing the subsoil for minerals and "trace-elements". Lucerne (alfalfa), for instance, an extremely useful fodder-legume, will penetrate the subsoil to a depth of 20 yards and more. Other types of what may be called humus-making machines are disc- and litter-ploughs, used in American "trash-farming" by chopping up straw and stubble and incorporating them in the topsoil to produce a spongy "crumb-structure".[1]

It follows that in ley-pastures sown with artificial grasses and legumes which, like the clovers, trap nitrogen from the air, a proportion both of deep-rooting grasses and medicinal herbs *or weeds* should always be included in the mixture. The customary commercial mixtures—though there are exceptions—fail to do so, with the result that the subsoil is not explored and the stock is under-nourished, preferring the weeds by the hedgerow to the most "progressive" leys.

Mr. Friend Sykes, who has written two books about his highly successful methods of organic farming on originally poor land upon the chalk highlands of eastern Wiltshire, uses no fewer than ten ingredients in his four-year ley-mixtures of grasses, clovers and deep-rooting herbs; among the last, yarrow, burnet and chicory:

> If the eight-year system (four ley and four arable) [he writes] we have laid down is followed then, with the assistance of subsoiling, the encouragement of the earthworm, the micro-organisms and the fungi of the soil, the mineral content of the soil will last indefinitely.

The return of the arable flock, penned or folded with hurdles, especially on thin chalk soils, we have already mentioned

[1] The recent invention of synthetic polyuranide and polysaccharide resins to replace the natural crumb-forming resins, a by-product of the decay of organic manures, will be useful or dangerous, depending upon how they are used: useful in preparing soil to receive composts or green-manure crops; dangerous if regarded as a substitute for them since, unlike compost, the synthetic resins release no nutrients as they decay and are intended solely to provide good surface texture.

in Chapter V. But pigs and other stock, especially poultry, can and should be used in folding units in the same manner; Mr. George Henderson, whose farm we mentioned in Chapter VI, together with Mr. Hugh Finn of Canterbury and others, have carried the folding of poultry over the land to the highest level of expert management. The deep-litter system of keeping poultry is another invention which piles up the manurial residues of the farm. Mixed stocking in grass orchards, again, should be universal in all the fruit counties, though only in Kent, our best-farmed county, is it a common practice. It is imperative in all our measures for redeeming farmlands to restore rotations and get away from monoculture both in crop and stock, a farming monstrosity to which our obsession with quantity and blindness to quality have made us all too prone. It was monoculture that made a dust-bowl of parts of the Middle West, just as it is monoculture in conifers that is destroying our watersheds. We ought, too, to consider the natural affinities between plants that actually occur in nature, especially among vegetables.

Does it work?, rather than *Will it pay?*, is an axiom that by the perversion of our farming system has become a revolutionary one, and to imagine that we can hope to respond to it merely by multiplying the number of tractors, cheapening the fertilizer bill and reckoning by "output per man", is the most pitiable of evasions. If the land is going bankrupt in humus, as it is, money and little or no food to buy with it, is the final logic of the situation. And to talk of this or that measure of self-defence against famine as too "expensive" is the bankruptcy of common sense. We have to adopt these and other methods of re-capitalizing the soil, regardless of "expense"; if the funds are lacking, then we must create them to meet an occasion that concerns our survival. Money must become the fertilizer of our endeavours, and our endeavours must be bent at all costs to replenish the fertility of the soil we have been squandering ever since we ceased to depend upon our own land to support us.

CHAPTER IX

Change and Education

In the preceding chapters of this work we have tried to show that our people really are confronted by the probability of famine; that we possess the fundamental resources to avoid this fate; that these resources are not being used because their existence is barely realized, so overlaid are they by both the physical artifacts and mental habits of our predecessors, who felt, thought and acted according to their belief that if there was one asset inexhaustible in this world, it was soil fertility; and one thing sure, it was the progress of man towards world peace and rational social and economic organizations.

Both of these fundamental assumptions having proved to be false, it is fitting that Britain should have to take the consequences, for it was in Britain that these assumptions were first formulated. That splendid arrogance resembled the moral quality which the Greeks called *hubris*; in Greek tragedy, reflecting Greek thought and feeling, whosoever was guilty of *hubris* became, by fatal law, the maker of his own *âte*, his own inevitable and terrible punishment. But there is a world of difference between the soul and mind of Western, European man, and those of Greek man; Western man believes in repentance and reform as effective in breaking the connection between crime and punishment. For Europeans since the Christian era, God is not implacable.

Britain can save herself, and in so doing show other peoples how to save themselves. She can do it by refounding the British community upon a sound, organic, self-renewing basis, using, to that end, the science, the mechanical power, the ingenuity and dexterity which have, hitherto, been squandered in the unworthy and unhappy muddle of a merely expedient industrialization.

Whenever the late H. G. Wells wanted to indulge himself and delight his readers with a vision of a rationally organized society, he could, as a novelist, clear away the obstructing muddle of *actual* society by inventing some tremendous catastrophe—a destructive comet, for example. Unless the sinister combination of irresponsible politics and subservient nuclear physics does our business for us with a few score atom bombs, we can anticipate no such wholesale destruction of the muddle we have inherited; we must clear it away. Moreover, we must do so in difficult conditions: we are like a charwoman on a wet day—when we want to do out the house we cannot dump all the furniture in the garden; we have to manage as best we can with the rooms all cluttered up. In short, to make a new society while we are clearing away the old one.

In remaking our society we have two sources of ideas to draw upon. The well-ordered, self-supporting societies of the past; and that future society which is implied by the existence of both the organic and mechanical sciences. As a means of demonstrating what we mean by this, let us suppose that the progress of electrical engineering had been more rapid than it was, and that by the time a great output of power from steam was available, the modern electrical generator and techniques for the distribution of electrical power had been developed. It is, of course, an impossibility, but there is no harm in pretending that it happened so.

In that event it is probable that there would have been no growth of vast industrial agglomerations. The English countryside need never have been depopulated, nor would the population have increased at so catastrophic a pace. The pattern of our industry has been made by the fact that mechanical power for industry could only be produced economically by units so massive that the workers had to be brought to the machine, the machine could not be taken to the workers. Moreover, the fuel for the production of steam power, coal, is so unhandy that it must be used as near to the mines as possible. It is true that the process of collecting together workers from workshops dependent upon local skills and materials, into huge factories, began before the rapid development of steam power. But it did so because the earliest mills were turned by water-power, a source of energy even less movable than steam. In the absence of electricity which can readily be supplied wherever it is needed, concentrations of workers into vast industrial areas sterilizing enormous surfaces of once fertile soil, is inevitable as soon as a manufacturing industry begins to grow.

The priority of steam traction, too, contributed towards the creation of a rigid system which imposed its rules on us, made us the servants of our industry. Railways are relatively inflexible; they impose their own social and economic pattern. They are like rivers; it is difficult and expensive to change their courses, and therefore necessary to group industry and commerce wherever they happen to run. Had the internal combustion engine preceded the steam-locomotive our whole modern society would have developed much more freely in the direction of our real, human interest, not in the direction of the interests of an industry and a commerce to which we were forced to conform.

While we were reasonably comfortable and well-fed inside the strait-jacket of nineteenth-century industrialism the temptation to continue wearing it was strong. It is true that great numbers of our people had to exist in misery and want; that we had been forced to degrade and foul vast areas of one of the most beautiful islands in the world, till they became hideous, dirty and poisonous slums. But the masters of industry were strong enough to force upon their workers, and upon the famers and land-owners, acceptance of the degradation of both land and men; acceptance of the slavery of children and women in mines and mills. It was sincerely believed—perhaps because men can always believe what it pays a profit to believe—that an economic law, as incalculable and harsh and unalterable as that of some cruel god, imposed upon industrial man certain kinds of behaviour. Probably no philosopher, or tyrant, no cosmic disaster has ever caused so much suffering to so many people, as that mild, learned and earnest economist, Adam Smith.

There was, of course, no such law. Economics is not a natural science, but an expedient one made by man. It has no laws which cannot be changed by will and idea.

From the fortuitous circumstance that steam power is relatively static, and from the absurd concept of economics as a natural science, have come our modern economic troubles and the foreseeable famine among the British people, because from these origins derive our patterns of thought and action in the application of labour to material resources. But we are not free simply to scrap the past and start on the future. We must have a plan as if we *could* do just that; but it must be realized in parts, not as a whole. What changes shall we have to make?

What, once again, are our objects? To feed the British people off the British soil and in so doing to restore to them a pleasant, dignified and meaningful way of life. What is the primary condition of such a way of life? That men be engaged in the making of things, whether works of thought, of art, of science, of craft, of industry, of agriculture, which are useful, plentiful and socially valuable. And how do we propose to do this? Firstly, by rejecting the false ways of thinking and acting imposed by steam-powered industry and "Liberal" economics and sociology. Secondly, by putting at the service of a new society the means made available by modern organic and mechanical science, not by the "dark Satanic mills" of the Victorians. To aim, in short, at making a people of farmers, craftsmen and artists emancipated from brutal and degrading toil by light machinery, and from the brutal and degrading social licence which is the proper name for capitalist-industrialist "freedom".

It is for this reason and because of these aims that we bring together Soil and Socialism in a single concept.

British Socialism has two origins: one of them is Marxist,

Continental; the other is Feudal, native. It looks forward to inheriting capitalist means of production; but it also looks backward to the ordered, disciplined and responsible, if narrow and short-sighted, society which preceded Capitalist society. Yet although, by reconciling these origins and allowing both to issue in its policy, it would provide itself with a real plan for the future society, it has, hitherto, failed to allow for this. The reason is easy to find: it has been so busy in ameliorating the conditions of life and work of the workers, in a sort of political, social and economic "make and mend", that it has had no time for social and political creation.

It is possible to suggest certain practical moves towards the end of putting first things first in a world which is no longer able or willing to allow us to put them anywhere else. Let us begin by ceasing to pretend, once and for all, that an ordered and responsible society is reconcilable with complete economic freedom, including the freedom to abuse land and soil. At present we give up certain economic liberties only reluctantly, and consoling ourselves with the pretence that we shall get them back again. It would be better to realize that most of these liberties—the liberty to abuse land, to exploit our fellow men, to gamble in supplies essential to life—are, in plain fact, socially pernicious: we have long been actually in danger of elevating the crimes committed against humanity by industrial capitalism into the elements of a social system.

If we recognize this, if we remember that the brief period of eighteenth- and nineteenth-century economic "freedom" was, in reality, an orgy of economic licence enabling a small number of men to run the community for their profit; if we remind ourselves that the private ownership of land is a relatively new and most inequitable departure from the long, sound doctrine of communal land ownership, it will be easier to accept the nationalization of land and its working by the nation's tenant-farmers under conditions of mutual responsibility. The new peasant will no longer be like the captain-owner of a ship picking up a living as best he can; he will be, in his relationship with the nation, like a Royal Navy captain—master of his vessel, certainly, but in the service of the nation.

One practical measure we can, should, absolutely must pass into law at once. To make certain that no more potentially food-bearing land is "sterilized" by any cause whatsoever, we need a short and didactic Act of Parliament by means of which it must become impossible, without special authorization, to use such land for any purpose whatsoever but agriculture. To build on agricultural land, to use it for military purposes, for recreational purposes, industrial purposes, any purposes but farming must be made as difficult as it once was to obtain a divorce. By the same Act, or by means of a separate Act, the Ministry of Agriculture must be given first refusal of all land or reclaimable surfaces which could be rehabilitated as farming land before they can be used for any other purpose. If these proposals seem extremist, it is because they are designed to help a nation which, perhaps within a lifetime, will otherwise be *in extremis*.

The next practical step to be taken is the initiation of a new kind of survey of our land resources, a survey not only of potential agricultural land, but also of land now occupied by industry. This survey should be carried out by a body of engineers, farmers, ecologists and industrialists. Its objects will be manifold: for example, it will suggest ways of using engineering really boldly to rehouse an expanding industry in a contracting surface space. We, more confident in science than those who pretend to a "scientific" point of view, believe that a vast area of the "black country" could be restored to agriculture if engineering were properly applied to the rehousing of industry in modern terms. The replacement of sprawling industrial slums by factories 1,000 feet tall is well within the means of our architects and industrial engineers, nor would such factories be any more vulnerable in war. Alternatively, and even more safely, let them go *down* 1,000 feet. For further example, we must ask our engineers to find means of building both civil and military airports—with their millions of acres of concrete, where wheat once grew—over water surfaces or on the roofs of industrial buildings. It is, in any case, the grossest inefficiency to separate our cities and their airports by miles of congested roads.

In the country, the surveyors will be asked to report on what "bad-lands" could be reclaimed, and how. Can Dartmoor be made to bear food? Of course it can. Can the mountains be terraced, the marshes and estuaries reclaimed? Of course they can. Other peoples in other times and with not one hundredth part of our means have done much more difficult things. Our scientists and engineers must cease to be timid at home and bold only abroad; they must become bold also at home. From Neolithic times until the 18th century the people of Britain were engaged in transforming their country physically to suit their needs. The process had, however, not been completed by any means when geographical and economic expansionism carried our creative energies overseas and turned Britain into a factory for supplying the newly colonized territories. But the time has now come to resume the work broken off in the 18th and 19th centuries. For overseas expansion is no longer possible or desirable.

In one way our position is very strong: we made our mistakes in countries other than our own. We know now that in reshaping a country we must work with nature, not against her; must make ourselves her partner, not her enemy. The work we have to do is not to wage a war ("The Conquest of Nature") but to create a work of art. And all great art is organic.

There is another lesson we have learnt: we cannot afford waste; not only such idiotic waste as the burning of coal in grates which yield less than 5% of the potential heat available, or waste of soil fertility, but waste of effort, of power, mind and muscle. This kind of waste is another derivative of our foolish respect for "economic freedom", a concept as stupid and dangerous as are those of political and social bondage. Thousands of tons of paper, of type metal, of ink; millions of kilowatts of power, thousands of brains and hands and eyes are continually engaged in, for example, the manufacture of pernicious rubbish in the form of crime, sex and sadism "comics"; in the operation of vast gambling schemes such as football pools. More millions of kilowatts of power, tons of material and human lives are consumed in the manufacture of other kinds of rubbish, less harmful morally, but economically wasteful. Why do we permit this kind of thing? Simply because someone is making a profit out of it. The only social service performed by football pools, for example, is that of giving every punter a very slender chance to buy his way out of the degrading industrial slavery to which we condemn him. It is significant that, with some exceptions, professional people with interesting and valuable work to do, do not gamble in this way—have no time for reading trash. We propose to give to every man and woman what was once their natural right: interesting, creative and valuable work to do.

Let us face the fact that we have hitherto failed completely to give to the majority of Western, industrial men any faith, any education, any future worth a tinker's curse. Yet we had the means to do all three. It is time we made use of them.

The means are: our knowledge of past societies, our consciousness of our own mistakes and our own guilt, and the unprecedented power to manipulate our environment conferred on us by science. And, of course, ourselves, the people.

Of all our problems, that of our own habits, our own timidity, our own conservatism in the worst sense, is the most difficult. How are we to find, among an industrial and commercial population, another 2 or 3 million farmers? For remember, if we are not only to feed ourselves but to employ ourselves sensibly, congenially, creatively, we cannot simply apply bigger and better machines to land; we have to repopulate our countryside with responsible, working farmers.

In the early stages of any such change as we have envisaged in this short book, an immense burden would necessarily be placed on the existing farmers. They and their men would, like regular soldiers in wartime, be the nuclei about which would be formed cadres of "national service" men. It is not difficult to make farmers out of gardeners and allotment-holders, given the will and the technical services. But in the beginning there would a period of improvization, of jury-rigging, while the nation attends to the really important task, the reorientation of education.

The education of a people reflects its economic and social states of mind. Our state of mind is still, despite food shortage, urban and industrial. Consequently, the education we give our children turns their minds away from the country, towards the town and the factory. They are, as it were, taught commercial geography, not agricultural geography, and so on throughout the curriculum. This is so much the case, that even village children are turned away from the rural environment. Not only are they carried, physically, away from the villages into the towns, to receive their education, but that education, such as it is, ignores the existence of the countryside.

There is observable a slight but definite reaction against this rule, initiated by schoolmasters, school inspectors, educationalists generally. A number of country schools have been associated with training-farms or gardens, and it has been found that children, particularly boys, become so interested in their farm-work that, if they can persuade their parents to pay their fares, they will travel considerable distances to attend such schools, where practical farming is part of the curriculum, passing over ordinary schools which are on their doorstep.

Every child ought, of course, for the sake of its health, happiness and early impressions, to be reared in the country or by the sea. This is not a practical possibility as yet. But it *is* possible to make sure that every child is brought into frequent contact with the agricultural countryside. And it is equally possible to multiply a hundredfold the number of rural schools which have small farms attached to them, run by the children and the staff.

But this is by no means the most important aspect of the

matter. What we have to do is to give agriculture the priority which properly belongs to it, even when we are teaching subjects which are not directly related to it. The "examples" in arithmetic and geometry should be drawn primarily from the farm. Biology can be given a bent towards practical horticulture and agriculture, geography should be taught quite as much in agricultural terms, as in commercial and topographical terms.

History, as taught in primary and secondary schools even today, is muddled, misleading and old-fashioned. The modern child might well be forgiven for agreeing with Jane Austen's Catherine Moreland that history "tells me nothing that does not either vex or weary me. The quarrels of popes and kings, with wars and pestilences in every page; the men all so good for nothing and hardly any women at all, it is very tiresome." No doubt, children should be given some idea of the political history of their own country, their own civilization, and even, if there were time, of all the others. But the history of man, and of nations, *is* the history of agriculture and stock-raising. On what did western civilization rise? On wheat and mutton. On what was Chinese culture founded? On rice. On what was the wealth of England founded? On wheat and wool. It is in terms of mankind as a farmer, a craftsman, an artist, that children should be taught history, not in terms of mankind as a ferocious killer and a liar and a cheat. For the young, let man be *Homo faber*, not *Homo militaris*.

Most important of all is the business of keeping the brightest boys for agriculture. Country boys and girls who show themselves more intelligent and quicker to learn than their fellows are invariably led by their teachers to look forward to an urban career. Yet a child, a man, can, today, give free expression to almost any talent but, perhaps, the fine arts, in the country just as well as in town. Farm management can absorb the "born organizer"; the Ministry of Agriculture would be all the better for a staff of country-bred civil servants; agricultural science calls for chemists, biologists, mycologists, engineers, electricians, botanists, statisticians. But, most important of all, the farm, especially the small farm, if it is to be fruitful, calls for the highest qualities of man, demands intuition as well as intelligence, *nous* as well as learning, tact as well as information. The good farmer is a whole man, an eclectic, and to supply his place we need the most brilliant of our children. It is the proper function of our most gifted citizens to lead and succour the others; succour and leadership today can come only from the land, once again to be at the service of our being and our continuing.

What we have written is not intended to be a plan for remaking our community. It is the reaction of two men to the desperate situation in which our country finds itself. About that, let there be no question. At the time of writing, our exports are sagging once again; for the twentieth time since the end of the war our frightened and inept politicians and businessmen scurry about in search of this or that expedient to supply our food and raw material. But this is nothing, it is only the beginning; at the risk of being tedious we repeat what others are also repeating: not only is Britain increasingly less able to get her living and fill her stomach by trade; the world population is rising by 20 millions a year and the world food resources shrinking by perhaps as many acres. The suggestion we have made is designed to feed ourselves; by so doing, to relieve the world larder of the responsibility for 25 million mouths; and in so doing, to make for ourselves a way of life, not physically easier, but morally, intellectually and socially healthier and less degrading than that which we have inherited.

Our suggestions may be impracticable, as they stand. Perhaps they can be modified to become workable. There is, certainly, one word which will be used as a stick with which to beat us: *realism*. But we believe ourselves to be the realists and those who will call us everything from idealists to cranks, to be the dreamers. They live in an ugly, crazy, cruel, dirty and failing world and they believe it, with monstrous cynicism, to be the only reality. But they are dreamers—and their dream is a nightmare.

It is our hope that they will wake in time to face our reality.

Envoi

In *l'Enracinement* (published in English as *The Need for Roots*[1]) Simone Weil, that fiery and heroic daughter of the French Resistance movement, whose vision, culture and philosophy far transcended it, put her finger on the fundamental evil of the modern age—rootlessness. We are displaced persons living on displaced soils. She has not been the only one to point this out, and the few who have seen that an organic refounding of scientific society can alone rescue modern man from a catastrophic end, will, by the pressure of events, become the many. But Simone Weil has been the only writer to invest the necessity for this dramatic change with a profound spiritual significance: she saw clearly that as modern man has created a world-wide dust bowl on earth, so he has created a dust-bowl of the spirit within himself.

We have been mainly concerned in this book with drawing attention to the narrowing of the margin which separates our country from famine, and with suggesting ways and means of checking this movement towards disaster, and of reversing it. But we are aware that it is not only our bodies which starve, and we believe that in putting forward certain tentative proposals for the refashioning of our society as an organic whole, instead of patching and tinkering with the out-of-date and inefficient and crazy machine which it now resembles, we make a contribution towards spiritual, as well as bodily salvation. Man can find satisfaction for the desire to make, to serve and to worship by being integrated into the whole of which landscape, soil, farm, workshop are working parts.

We believe that there is no way of avoiding famine while maintaining our integrity as a people, excepting by such means as we have suggested. But we also believe that the soul of the

[1] Routledge and Kegan Paul, 1952.

nation, and of more than the nation, is the greater prize to be won: the escape from the triviality and vulgarity which degrade, into the responsibility and dignity which elevate.

For, a people which neglects or ignores the desire and the need to root itself once again in its soil, is inviting a harsh judgment both in body and in soul.